To Douglas from u̶ ̶ ̶ ̶ ̶ ̶ ̶ ̶
aunt Betty — ch ◁

WILD TREASURE

THE STORY OF DAVID DOUGLAS

Wild Treasure

THE STORY OF DAVID DOUGLAS

by Adrien Stoutenburg and Laura Nelson Baker

CHARLES SCRIBNER'S SONS   NEW YORK

To

Senator Hubert H. Humphrey,

a friend of our nation's natural resources

D-9.65[H]

PRINTED IN THE UNITED STATES OF AMERICA

Library of Congress Catalog Card Number 58-10637

AUTHORS' NOTE

In writing this book we have relied on David Douglas' own journals as our chief source material. Other helpful information was found in articles in the Oregon Historical Society's publications; an adult biography, *Douglas of the Fir,* by Athelstan George Harvey; *Seventy-five Years in California,* by William Heath Davis; manuscript letters from Douglas to Governor DeWitt Clinton in the files of the Columbia University Libraries; and the Archives of California, Bancroft Library, University of California.

As there seems to be disagreement between sources as to the date of Douglas' birth, the statement in his own diary and the date on his tombstone have been followed.

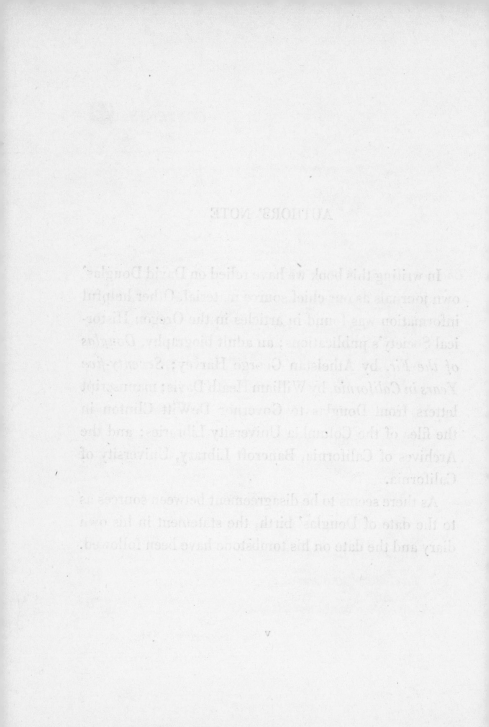

CONTENTS

Chapter One

Hawk's Nest

Morning mist lay like white smoke on the river and clung to the sloping fields. It made a crooked wreath around the crest of Kinnoul Hill and brushed at the faces of two boys walking along a footpath, schoolbooks in hand. In the dew-wet grass, their bare feet left dark imprints.

The younger boy, David, was ten, his brother John a few years older. John's footprints went straight and steadily toward the schoolhouse at the base of the big hill but David stopped constantly. His blue eyes searched the ground, the sky, the nearby hills, and the misty peaks of the Highlands farther on to the north and west.

John called back impatiently, "Hurry on, Davy. I

1

canna wait for you if you keep lagging behind to look
at every wee flower in the brush!"

David looked up from his inspection of a plant beside the path. His face beneath a thatch of reddish-
gold curly hair was pink with excitement. "But look,
John. It is no ordinary flower. See—"

"You may like the feel of Master Wilson's taws on
your back, but not I." John strode on with exaggerated
firmness though he glanced back hopefully.

David hesitated, studying the pale yellow blooms at
his feet. His back was still sore from the last time he
had been punished, just for daydreaming. The time
before that had been for studying a strange winged
insect that had flown into the schoolroom, instead of
translating the Latin in his copy book. And back at
the old school in Scone . . . He sighed and stood up.
If he spent the time thinking of all the lickings and
scoldings he had had, he would be late for certain. He
seized one of the yellow blooms and ran after his
brother.

As he caught up to John, he put the bloom carefully between the leaves of his book where other faded
flowers were already stored: hyacinths and violets, scraps
of grass and brightly colored weeds. Even a feather
from a bird's wing fluttered from one page. "After

lessons, I'll take my flower over to Mr. Beattie at the gardens," David said. "He'll know its name."

"What difference is it to you what its name is?"

"I just like to know."

"Aye, and if you don't study more at school there's little else you will know. Maybe you'll even get thrown out of school again, the way you were back in the other school."

"I couldna help myself," David said, sighing. "The old dame there wanted me to sit fast at a wooden desk all day, learnin' nothing but words and numbers."

"How else can you be a scholar?"

The harsh clang of a bell sounded, cutting across the gayer sounds of birds and the distant bleating of sheep in the mountain pastures.

"There's the warning bell," John said. "Race you, Davy."

David spurted forward, his sturdy legs matching their strength against his brother's longer ones. John was one of the fastest runners in Perthshire. John nearly always won, unless he deliberately slowed down, but the sport was worth it for the trying.

Something flashed among the trees along the Tay river. David stopped, seeing the orange bill and pink shanks of an oyster-catcher as the bird whipped by.

And directly above, up where the mist was shredding into wisps as thin as silver hair against an increasingly blue sky, a hawk was wheeling slowly around Kinnoul's summit. The hawk's nest was up there, David remembered, full of eggs that might be hatching out even as he stood here wasting time.

Sunlight broke through a remaining cloud, lighting the whole landscape around him, touching even the dreary schoolhouse with gold. He saw his brother dart inside and heard Master Wilson's scratchy voice call out: "And where is your brother, Master John Douglas? Has he lost hisel' on the way again?"

The hawk circled lower. The oyster-catcher flashed among the trees again. From the moors came the sound of the curlews calling, two silver notes followed by deep and silver-sounding trills. The trill echoed in David's heart like a thin trumpet call. It made even his naked toes tingle. Along the green slope of the hill the deep, damp grass would welcome his running feet.

He wheeled, facing the slope that went up and up over seven hundred feet above the plain. He could study his books later. A day like this might not come again soon. Mist could thicken into rain and the sky could be dour with clouds. Anyhow, there were things to be learned that were in none of the books he owned, not even in the books he read over and over for pleasure, like *Sinbad the Sailor* and *Robinson Crusoe.*

I can teach myself! he thought and remembered his father's answer to that. *He that teaches himsel' has a fule for his maister.*

Well, then, perhaps the hawks and the owls and the river and the moors could be teachers. Teachers without whips in their hands!

He paused, his back muscles tensing, and looked toward the school. A long, lean figure stood in the doorway and on the clear air came Master Wilson's voice crying, "Davy! Davy Douglas—if ye don't come back this instant, you'll get a hiding that'll beat some knowledge into ye."

David took a step forward, then stopped, a stubborn line forming around his round, full chin. I'll get one anyhow, now, he reflected. The hawk swooped through the air once more, and David went on, running. The sight of baby hawks in a nest would be worth the master's stripes.

Panting, he reached the summit at last, his schoolbook still clasped in one perspiring hand. His feet were stained with grass and bruised from the numberless agate-gleaming pebbles on the hill. A thorn had made a rent in his breeches and scratched one cheek.

Holding his hand to the scratch, he stood and looked at the world around and below. It glistened from one horizon to another. There, in the distance, were the peaks of the Grampians. He recited the names of the highest ones aloud, lingering over the sounds. "Ben-y-Gloe, Beinn Dearg, Cairn Toul, Ben Macdhui—" He could see the glimmering Tay, softly flowing on through the green Carse of Gowrie, winding in and out among fields and orchards, heading at last toward the sea. Below was the city of Perth. Three miles beyond was his family's cottage, with the stone castle and the gardens nearby.

He remembered the flower in his book and took it out. William Beattie, his father's friend, was the head gardener of the Earl of Mansfield's estate. Mr. Beattie would know the flower's name. Maybe even young McGillivray who helped Beattie in the gardens would know. David was envious of McGillivray and the boys not much older than himself who were employed in the gardens. Mr. Beattie had said there might be an opening for a "likely lad" some day soon. Maybe, if Papa would ask him again and put in a word for him . . .

David looked at the path leading homeward and pictured himself trudging the three miles back with still another confession of having played the truant from school, and shook his head. His father was apt to send him off to bed without even a sip of broth.

The golden sun poured through the fading mist and the world sparkled until he felt like a cup filled to the brim. "I canna help it," he declared, as if the hill had ears to hear, and he began running toward the rocks where the hawk's nest was hidden, stopping to look and peer and inspect every new plant and bloom and thorn along the way. More leaves and blossoms found their way into his Latin book, while David hummed to himself. When the book grew so fat with plant specimens that it spilled out more than it held, he laughed and picked them up again.

Here on Kinnoul Hill the world was perfect and he was as free as the golden eagle that sometimes fanned its wings between this and Moncrieff Hill. As for Papa, hadn't he seen him one day lay down his stonemason's hammer to go picking daisies for Mother? David remembered the sight of the bright petals in his father's gnarled, brown hands. They were kind hands and tender, for all he did not believe in sparing the rod.

There! The shaggy hawk's nest was just ahead. He crept forward, aware of nothing in the world now but that.

The flower in David Douglas' book grew withered and dry without his ever having had a chance to show it to Mr. Beattie. There were other things to do in life besides finding out the name of every bloom that grew. Peat must be cut for burning, water hauled from the well, chickens must be fed and the eggs collected, and the cows milked. Even though David and John divided the chores between them, and the sisters helped with the cleaning and knitting and cooking indoors, there was always something that needed doing.

For David there was the extra chore of finding food for his growing collection of wild things: mice for the young owl he had found and kept, bullock's liver for the baby hawks he had transported from Kinnoul Hill. The bullock's liver cost money and often he spent his daily penny for that instead of for the bread that was to be his school-day lunch. Trudging home the long miles from school, he sometimes scarcely felt the soreness from some recent punishment as much as the pangs of hunger in his stomach.

Sundays were no better. David's father forbade any excursions to the woods or hills on the Sabbath, and David obeyed that rule. Sunday was a time for reading the Bible and attending services at the new parish kirk at New Scone. The kirk and the cottages, including the one in which David had been born in 1799, had been moved from the site that was once the capital of Scotland, the Royal City of Scone, now called Old Scone. The castle, where Scottish kings had been crowned, had also been rebuilt, its towers and halls, its 125 rooms, and its magnificent grounds making it one of the finest in the country.

When he could steal the time, David wandered near the garden gates, trying to see what went on inside. Sometimes he saw finely-dressed men and women wandering over the grass or the walks that enclosed beds of luxuriant flowers, fruit trees, or vegetables. He looked with wonder at hedges of box or holly clipped into the shapes of birds or animals, and looked with a faint shiver at a famous sycamore tree. Queen Mary, the very queen who had lost her head under the executioner's blade, had planted the sycamore. Most of all, however, David watched the gardeners at work, pruning and planting and weeding, the hunger in his spirit greater than any hunger his stomach had known. What must it be like to work among such green and growing richness! He left off his daydreams with a sigh. The common wildflowers and the heather would have to be his garden.

One cool evening in late spring, when the wind was sucking at the chimney, there was a knock at the door.

David, sitting on a stool near the flickering oil cruise on the table, was bending a pin to make a fishhook. His mother was tucking the baby into his cradle in a darker corner of the room and his father was busy sharpening a stone chisel. David looked up in surprise at the knock; it was hardly a night for callers. His mother started for the door but David's father waved her back.

"I'll answer, Jean. Most likely it's Tom Carlisle come to order a tombstone for poor Annie." He laid down the chisel and went to the door.

David's oldest sister whispered to John, "Maybe it's the schoolmaster comin' to tell on Davy again." The two other sisters exchanged worried glances.

"Whist, now!" Mrs. Douglas said. "No whispering and snickering. Janey, push your hair out of your eyes. Davy, stop fiddling with that pin." The baby whimpered and she rocked the cradle mechanically, while she gestured to one of the girls to put some fresh fuel on the hearth fire. "Whoever 'tis, they'll be wanting a cup of tay."

"Evenin', John," a man's voice in the outside darkness said. "I wanted to have a word with you about your Davy."

David pushed the bent pin swiftly into his pocket, thinking about the big salmon he had pulled out of the water near Mr. Richardson's fishery just yesterday. Mr. Richardson didn't like to have people fishing on his property, not when he was in the business of catching all the salmon himself so that he could sell them to the villagers at a high price. The pin pricked David's finger and he gave a small gasp.

His mother, mistaking the cry for one of guilt, looked at him sadly. "Davy, Davy, what new mischief have you done?"

"None, Mother," David answered earnestly. "At least, none that seemed like mischief when I did it."

John grinned and Janey clapped her hand to her mouth as the visitor stepped in.

David felt warm with relief when he saw that the visitor was big, gruff, red-cheeked William Beattie. He started up to get the book with the pressed flower specimens in it, but his mother warned him to sit still.

"And how is the family and yoursel', Mr. Douglas?" Beattie said, removing his hat. He looked around the one-room cottage with approval. "It's a cozy house that keeps out the bluster of the wind on such a night." He sat down on the bench that Mr. Douglas pushed forward and pulled out his pipe.

"You'll have a cup of tay with your pipe, Will?" Mr. Douglas asked.

"Nay, thanking you, I've not the time." Again Mr. Beattie looked around the room. This time his gaze settled on David and the expression in his eyes made David's skin prickle suddenly the way it did when he saw some unfamiliar bird or flower shining in the distance. Mr. Beattie's gaze traveled to John. "Your lads are growing up," he observed.

"Aye. Young John's to be apprenticed to an architect soon," Mr. Douglas said, squatting on his heels near the hearth and stuffing tobacco into his own pipe. "As for Davy—what was it you wanted to say about Davy?"

There was a momentary silence in which David could hear the loud thumping of his heart above the creaking of the cradle.

Beattie sucked on his pipe. "Only that I could set him to some potting and digging in the gardens if he's not afraid of work, and maybe he could learn a little from it all on the side."

Only! David leaped from his stool. "Just try me, sir! I'll work day and night. And I'll learn!"

"Not so quick, lad," his father said. "Back to your chair." To Beattie he said, "Davy's no great hand to study. I canna lie about that, Will. But as for digging for plants—and pulling them up, as well—he can do that right enough if that's a recommendation."

John, who had been struggling to keep silent, burst out: "He only pulls them up to study, and he's planted

more in the little plot in back than he pulls. And there's
nobody in the whole shire who knows more about such
things—excepting Mr. Beattie."

"Aye," Mr. Douglas said, "but this will not be picking posies for play."

"But, Papa—" David began.

"Mr. Beattie and I will discuss the matter without
your help, Davy, or you either, John." He turned back
to Beattie. "Davy has his virtues, to be sure, but there
is no use trying to cover up his vices. He's not one to
wear a harness well. When it comes to discipline and
routine, now . . ." He sighed.

"He's not afraid to spend hisel', John," Mrs. Douglas
spoke up from her corner. "Davy's a good boy."

"With a bit of the devil mixed in," the father said
with painful honesty.

Beattie leaned closer to the hearth and sat looking at
the smoky flames. "I like a devil better than a dolt." He
stood up. "Be at the big gate tomorrow, lad. I'll start
you out working in the flower garden under McGillivray.
You'll be beginning at the bottom. How high up you go
depends on you."

Joy swelled David's chest and throat to the point of
pain. Half-choking with gratitude, he stammered his
thanks, and then, in the same breath, said, "I've a wee

flower I found—I've been hoping to ask, for weeks, what it might be." He got up, turning toward the rough shelf over his and John's bed.

"You mustn't pester Master Beattie with questions now, Davy," his mother murmured. "Tomorrow—"

But David already had the withered flower in his hand. "Is it rare, sir? I have never seen its like before." He looked at it ruefully. "It was like a tiny star in the grass before it shriveled."

Beattie took the flower in his callused hand and held it to the light of the oil cruise. "So you find stars in the grass, do you, Davy? And are you thinking you can find a new kind of flower that somebody would name after you?"

"Oh, nay! I wouldn't dream of that."

The head gardener handed the bloom back to Davy.

"And what is it, sir?"

"I canna say for sure, though it resembles one of the saxifrages."

"They say that up in the high hills there is a certain kind of saxifrage that is the only one of its kind in all of Scotland or in Britain, either."

Beattie nodded. "And do you know its Latin name?"

Mrs. Douglas said apologetically, in Mr. Beattie's direction, "Davy is weak on Latin," even as David said quickly:

"Aye, sir. It is the *saxifraga cernua*. Or so it says in the book the tobacconist in Perth let me look at one day."

There was a brief silence. John grinned and winked at Janey. Mrs. Douglas tried to keep the pride from shining in her face, and Mr. Douglas worked his mouth around his pipestem as if he were trying to keep a pleased smile from getting a start.

Mr. Beattie put his hat back on his head and said simply, "I'll see you on the morrow, Davy. Good night to ye all, and good weather." Then he was gone, the door closing against him and the wind.

At once, the children were shunted off to bed so as "not to waste the morning light in sleep."

David, lying on the straw-filled tick beside John, stared wide-eyed at the hearth-flickering darkness. His mind raced far beyond the night and the morning and all the other mornings to come. A flower named after him some day? His head was getting big already even to think of such a thing. Anyhow, in so small a country as Scotland there could scarcely be many new plants that had not already been discovered. But he had heard the gardeners talk of strange and beautiful plants that grew in other parts of the world. Sometimes travelers brought back seeds from across the ocean, seeds from Australia and Europe and America. Perhaps some day he, too, could sail to lands far away. . . .

He closed his eyes, trying to shut out the visions and long dreams that went tumbling through his head. He had enough to do, starting tomorrow, without thinking up even bigger things. Yet, perhaps one had to think big things even to do the little ones right.

The wind circled the cottage, whining at the rough stone walls. Out in its pen, his pet owl made a hooting cry and David remembered with a pang that he had forgotten to feed it. He got up stealthily and went out, carrying crumbs of bread he had saved from his own meal and hidden under his bed.

Chapter Two

A Far Horizon

The dingy hall, set in the center of factories, slowly filled with young men. Many of them were medical students who had to attend the botany lectures as a part of their course of study. On the lecture platform the new Regius Professor of Botany at Glasgow University stood looking at his notes as the young men took seats in front of him.

Near a window that admitted a little smoky morning light into the small room, David Douglas, too, waited eagerly for Professor William Jackson Hooker to begin. His trousers were baggy at the knees and there was a trace of damp soil on them, from kneeling on the ground. At the tip of his straight nose was a yellow smudge of pollen.

17

"Ready for another good lecture, Douglas?" a voice said.

David turned to see one of the medical students, John Scouler. "A great lecture, you mean."

Scouler nodded and took a place beside Douglas. "You'd never believe this was Hooker's first teaching post."

"I have a hard time believing I'm here at all," Douglas said. He looked at the tall, handsome professor up front, and the blackboard that before long would be covered with Hooker's drawing of plants. This was a continuation of a dream that had begun that morning ten years before in Scone when he had first begun to work in the Mansfield gardens. Work and study, for seven years, until he had learned all he could from McGillivray and William Beattie and the Browns of the Perth Nursery. And books—books that he had begged and borrowed from every available source. First Lee's *Introduction to Botany* and Donn's *Catalogue*. Then Nicol's *Gardener's Calendar* and the publications of the Horticultural Society of London. And finally, the books from Sir Robert Preston's own library, Sir Robert whose private garden at Valleyfield was one of the best in Scotland.

He glanced at the botanical volume lying on his knee

now and smiled. There were no welts on his back these days! Nor had there been during the winter of private school in Perth when he had labored over Latin again, and arithmetic. After two years of working in Sir Robert Preston's gardens he had become foreman and received an appointment to the staff of the Glasgow Botanical Gardens. He knew then that he would be more than a gardener. He would be a botanist. Like Carl Linnaeus, the great Swede who had first worked out a useful system for classifying flowers and shrubs and trees and mosses. Or like the British botanists, Robert Morison and John Ray, Nehemiah Grew and Stephen Hales.

The names of the pioneers in botany sang in his mind as he listened to Professor Hooker. There was so much to learn, to read, to listen to, and to discover. His brain felt like a hive of bees. He fidgeted on his seat, from inner excitement.

John Scouler looked at him and smiled, a kindred excitement burning in his own eyes. Hooker had a gift for setting imaginations leaping and for sharing with his listeners the enthusiasm he felt for the mysterious, secret lives of the green and growing things.

"—and build a great garden," Hooker was saying, "here in the very heart of Glasgow. By next year we hope to have 9,000 different species represented, species brought from all over the world by our fellow-laborers in the field."

Fellow-laborers. It was a term Hooker often used in addressing co-workers and students.

"With almost every ship," Hooker went on, "bringing merchandise and raw materials, comes some new plant. For example . . . " He pointed to one of the many large, colored drawings that hung around the room, drawings he had made himself. "Here is a fern recently brought from America—by a naval officer. And over here is a rose from India brought by a missionary. While here, from Africa . . . "

America. India. Africa. Douglas thought of world travelers and the men appointed by the London Horticultural Society to go and seek new plant species in far away lands. If ever such luck came his way . . . He cut short his extravagant dreams. There was more than enough to do right here in this humming city. He fastened his attention on Hooker again while he fingered in his waistcoat a folded piece of blotting paper which held a dried flower. Soon Hooker would ask for an analysis of specimens. This was the most interesting part of the hour to Douglas, despite his shyness before the class and its visitors.

When Hooker said, "And now, I welcome any stu-

dent who wishes to come forward with one of the specimens I recently distributed among you," Douglas got
to his feet.

"If the class would be interested, sir, I should like to
discuss this herb, the red rot."

Hooker nodded, a speculative gleam in his eye.
"Come forward. First I'll sketch your red rot, so-called,
on the board." With a few quick glances at the specimen
Douglas presented, Hooker sketched the herb, then
turned to a young man in the front row. "What do you
call this herb, Edmonds?"

The youth concentrated. "Uh, *drosera ro—rotund—*"

"No, not the Latin; the common name, please."

"Why, we call it moor-gloom, at home, sir."

"Your home is Yorkshire, then?"

"Yes, sir."

"But if you were from Devonshire," Hooker said,
"you would call it a flycatcher. If from Somerset, a fly-
trap, or a stickyback. If from Donegal, an oil plant.
Douglas, here, calls it red rot. Now, Edmonds, give the
Latin so we can all call it by one name."

"*Drosera rotundifolia,*" Edmonds said promptly this
time.

Hooker looked at Douglas somberly. "I'm afraid
you'll have to learn to be more precise when you name

a plant or we shall have more confusion than we already
have."

Although Hooker's manner was kindly and even teas-
ing, the reprimand was keener than the taws to Douglas'
sensitivity. The general titter that ran around the room
did not help, either. His face flushed a deep red and he
found himself stammering as he tried to describe the
different parts and characteristics of the plant. When he
was through, he went stumbling back to his chair, feeling that he had made a fool of himself in front of the
class and, worse, in front of the one man he most wanted
to impress.

He bumped blindly against Scouler who had risen to
speak about the medical properties of the herb. "It was
supposedly of great value in consumption and swoon-
ing," Scouler said, "and for faintness of the heart. The
dew constantly on its leaves, in spite of the sun, was
supposed to have the power to keep men's bodies from
drying or withering. " . . .

Douglas slumped in his chair, too miserable to listen
to the other students adding scraps of knowledge to the
discussion of the *drosera rotundifolia*. He knew the Latin
name as well as anyone. What had made him blurt out
that ridiculous "red rot"? Well, it was too late now.
He lifted his head and saw that the majority of the stu-

dents had their hands raised, and that Hooker was looking at him.

"I confess I'm surprised, Douglas," Hooker said,
"that you show such lack of interest in a field trip."

"Field trip?" Douglas echoed stupidly as Hooker
began to count the upraised hands.

Scouler leaned near, whispering, "Put your hand up,
man. Quick! It's more than a field trip around Glasgow.
An excursion to the Bredalbane range in the Highlands—"

Douglas leaped to his feet. "Aye!" he called out.
"That is, please, sir—I wish to be counted, too!"

Hooker gave the faintest of nods and Douglas sat
down again, flushing, nervous perspiration moistening
his palms. Had Hooker actually seen and heard him or
was the nod for someone else? There had been occasions when he had thought Hooker singled him out for
special attention on the regular Saturday field trips to
nearby points and he had dared to dream that he and
the professor might become close friends.

As Hooker dismissed the group, Douglas marched up
front, determination in his step in spite of his inner
nervousness.

"Sir," he said, facing Hooker, "I canna bear not
knowing for sure whether you are including me in the
excursion."

Hooker smiled and laid a hand on David's shoulder. "I counted you in before you counted yourself, lad." He reached for his hat. "I'm on my way over to the herbarium. Perhaps you'd like to stroll along."

Clapping his own hat on his head, Douglas hurried along at the tall professor's side, out among the factories and reeking chimneys. In the dredged-out mouth of the river Clyde they could see ships at anchor and in the distance loomed the summits of the Campsie and Kilpatrick hills. Douglas and Hooker walked for almost two full minutes before Douglas managed to say, "I can't tell you, sir, what a great honor it is to be asked—to be able to walk and talk with you."

Hooker paused, looking at a ragged bit of vegetation forcing its way through a crack in a house wall. He shook his head. "The honor is to be a laborer in the fields of truth. And you never know where you will find it—on a mountain top or growing out of a dingy crack like this humble plaintain here. Never be too proud to stoop." He bent down and plucked a leaf, handing it to Douglas.

Douglas' mouth quirked up at one corner. "*Plantago major*, you mean, sir?"

Hooker looked at him sharply and for an instant Douglas was afraid he had been too bold. Suddenly

Hooker laughed. Douglas joined in and they went on, their mingled laughter sounding above the city's din.

In late June, Douglas and thirty other students took off for the Highlands with Hooker, each carrying a small supply kit, a tin collecting-box called a vasculum, and apparatus for drying plants. For Douglas each step upward over the flowering moors and the blossom-starred mountainsides brought some new interest and delight so that he could scarcely hold himself back from rushing away to explore alone. But he kept close to Hooker, making note of everything the professor did, listening to all he said. Often he was rewarded by Hooker's smile or praise. At night, when they camped in the open, he and his friend John Scouler discussed everything from a curious bit of lichen to the giant bears, called grizzlies, which roamed the western part of America.

"I think I'd rather be sent to look for plants in America than anywhere else," Douglas said one night, stretching out comfortably on a bed of fern.

"And get scalped by savages?"

"What good would my scalp do them? Anyway, I'll probably be old and bald before I ever get a chance to go."

"You've scarcely started to shave, let alone worrying about your old age," Scouler laughed.

"I'm nineteen already," Douglas said. "Hooker was only twenty when he discovered a species of moss that had never been known in Britain before."

"Aye. *Buxbaumia aphylla.*"

"Not to mention botanizing in Iceland when he was but twenty-four."

"And losing all of his collection, and almost his life, when the ship burned."

"Fires or scalping, I'd welcome the risks," Douglas said.

"Folly is a bonny dog," Scouler commented. "I would risk the same for the sake of medicine."

They both lay looking up at the stars, trying to read their futures in the blue-white constellations wheeling overhead.

"Though I'd welcome South America, too," Douglas said.

A new voice spoke from the darkness. "Have you learned all there is to know in Scotland so soon?" The figure of Professor Hooker went on by, checking the sleepers, before Douglas had a chance to answer. He looked back at the stars. It was not the first time that the professor had commented on his impatience. At the same time, Hooker had also praised him for zeal. Where did zeal leave off and impatience begin?

It was a question Douglas asked himself often in the weeks and months that followed. When his labors in the Botanical Gardens brought him a word of approval from the gardens' curator, Stewart Murray, he decided it was zeal. When, in his eagerness to accomplish the work of ten men, he made some blunder, he decided it was impatience.

Once, one of the other gardeners said, "Ye must watch your headlongness, man. Some day ye may rush into that from which you canna get out again."

Perhaps. In the meantime, nods of approval from both Murray and Hooker were far more frequent than frowns. And in the fall of the same year as the excursion to the Bredalbane range, Hooker invited Douglas to accompany him with a much smaller party to Ben Lomond, the mountain by Loch Lomond.

Walking the streets of Glasgow, Douglas felt that he was one of the luckiest young men in Scotland.

The trip to Lomond was only the beginning. In the following summers he was often Professor Hooker's only companion on trips not only to the Highlands but to the Isles and up the mighty crag of Ben Nevis. Together they searched along the silver shores of lochs and collected plants in fragrant glens, pausing at night to sleep in some shepherd's hut or a handy hayloft. And as they shared the hardships and glories of the trail, Douglas knew that he had found not only a great teacher but a great friend.

For his part, Hooker watched and appraised his young comrade, studying him with the same close attention he might have given a rare plant. There was something rare in this young Scot, a quality of single-minded devotion that made him seem destined for permanent achievement in the world of botany. Douglas did not even spare time for the lassies who sometimes sought his glance. He went stubbornly, almost fanatically, on his way. And yet, there was a gentleness in the curve of his smile that made one forget the moments when his chin set in a mood that was headstrong to the point of rebellion.

A scientific colleague, discussing Douglas with the Professor one day, suggested, "I know what you mean, Hooker. A sweet fanatic. The kind of lad who, if he can't get somewhere on his feet, will crawl on his knees."

A sweet fanatic, Hooker thought. Yes. Perhaps. At any rate, a young man to watch, and to help if the opportunity came.

The opportunity came sooner than either Hooker or Douglas expected. In the spring of 1823, Joseph Sabine, the secretary to the Horticultural Society in London, sat talking to some of his associates about the need for able men who could be sent abroad to search for new species for the Society's garden at Chiswick. Three thousand fruit trees bloomed in its orchards, twelve hundred varieties of roses, dozens of ornamental shrubs, together with vegetables and new, curious plants from remote countries across the oceans. Still, this was a mere beginning, for the thirty-three-acre garden had been started only the year before. Rare specimens were in demand among gardeners and scientists everywhere, often bringing high prices in the market place.

"We want hardy young men," Sabine said. "Men who are well-trained in botany and not afraid to face danger or endure hardships. We especially need men to go to China."

"What about some of Professor Hooker's pupils in Glasgow?"

Sabine nodded. He already had his friend Hooker in mind as the person to consult. John Goldie, one of Hooker's students, had done a good job of collecting in the eastern United States and in Canada a few years before. "I'll ask Hooker," Sabine said.

When Hooker received Sabine's message, he called Curator Murray aside. "Murray, I'm thinking of robbing you of David Douglas. I'm going to recommend him to Joseph Sabine as a scientific collector."

Murray let out his breath in a rueful sigh. "But he's my head gardener now. It would be a sore loss."

"Too sore for you to add your recommendation to mine?"

"Well—nay, how could I refuse?" He looked toward a spot of the garden where Douglas was at work, the sun blazing down upon the young man's red-gold hair. "Anyhow, if I don't give Douglas a push, he'll simply push up without my help. The knotty problem, Professor, is how to recommend him enough. He's a braw lad. The best."

Back in his study, Hooker wrote out his own recommendation, mentioning Douglas' "great activity, undaunted courage, and singular zeal" which marked him as "an individual eminently calculated to do himself credit as a scientific traveler."

He sealed the letter and sighed. Other young men had sailed to strange lands in pursuit of green treasure and never returned. Opportunity was also risk. Risk not only to Douglas but to himself, for with the posting of the letter he might well be losing a companion, a fellow laborer in the quest for truth, whom he had come to love.

There was no help for it. He called his secretary. "Tell Master Douglas I want to see him."

In a matter of minutes Douglas appeared, the usual smudge of earth on his cheek, the juices of plants staining his fingers.

Hooker tapped the envelope lying on his desk. "I've just written to Sabine in London recommending you as a collector in China." He added with a faint smile, "Unless you have some objection."

Douglas said nothing for a moment. He felt dazed. He reached for his teacher's hand. "I'll never forget this day, sir," he said then. "And I'll never forget you. Wherever I go, whatever I find, I'll bring it back to you and the Glasgow gardens."

"Not to me, lad. You'll be working for the London Society now. They'll have first claim."

Douglas realized that what Hooker said was true. Whatever seeds or plants he might discover would have to be sent to London and not Glasgow. "Aye, I know." He smiled shyly at his friend. "But it is you who'll have first claim on my thoughts—and in my heart."

There was a strained silence for a moment. Then Hooker said, "If you find any red rot in China—"

Douglas laughed, then added seriously, "If I find something new, it will surely be given your name, sir." Thanking Hooker again, he excused himself. "I must write my father and mother and my brother John, and my sisters—" He paused for breath, "and my friends at Valleyfield and Perth and Dunfermline."

"You are excused," Hooker said.

Douglas rushed out, his hair and coattails flying. He must write to everyone. He wanted to tell the whole, wide, waiting world.

Chapter Three

American Harvest

David Douglas leaned over the rail of the sailing ship, watching the rain fall in a gray haze over the grayer Atlantic. He was heading, not for China but for North America. The Society's plans had been changed because of hostilities in China between the English and the natives. There might be too much risk, Sabine had said.

America, Douglas thought, remembering his and Scouler's conversation months ago. Near him a dog was eagerly licking the moist deck. A week out of Liverpool, water had been rationed, two quarts to a passenger. Douglas called the dog and patted him, wishing he had brought along a pet of his own.

Each day his impatience to be done with the ocean trip mounted. He had not been seasick while the *Ann Maria* had tossed in contrary winds in the English Chan-

nel, but he found the days of slow travel increasingly
tedious. At first he had been able to study clouds of sea
fowl that hovered over the ship and great schools of por-
poises that surrounded it. While passing the Azores,
Captain Tair had loaned him his spyglass and Douglas
had been able to see small shrubs on one of the islands,
but he had not been able to land for a closer look. Now
there was little to do except keep his diary, read his
botanical books, and study a Spanish grammar that
Sabine had recommended. Some day, Sabine had said,
Douglas might be sent to a Spanish-speaking country.

There would be few Spanish-speaking people where
he was going now, he reflected, compared to Dutch, English and other Europeans who had settled the eastern
part of the United States.

He looked westward, thinking of that vast area, the
American West, and of the exploration party under Meri-
wether Lewis and William Clark. They had gone all the
way to the west coast, at the direction of President Jefferson, and when they returned after two years they had
brought back new plants and seeds to be studied and
classified. Douglas' own trip seemed tame to him by com-
parison. His orders were to concentrate on orchards, not
wilderness areas.

His thoughts were interrupted by the moan of a horse.

A short, worried-looking man went toward the passage-way to a lower deck.

"He's going to lose that horse of his," another pas-senger said to Douglas. "Sick as sin, it is, poor thing. Two hundred pounds he paid for its passage, too." He shook his head and pressed his hand to his stomach. "This sea is enough to make anybody sick." He looked at Douglas. "Doesn't bother you, though, does it? Well, you're young."

"For the time being," Douglas said with a smile. He had celebrated his twenty-fourth birthday on ship-board, duly noting the date in his diary: June 25, 1823.

He went to his quarters, opened his copy of Thomas Nuttall's *Genera of North American Plants,* and soon lost himself in study. Nuttall, a Yorkshireman, had spent many years in America, part of the time as instructor in botany at Harvard University. Douglas had hopes of meeting him.

Now and then, through the sounds of the masts creak-ing above decks, came the cry of the sick horse. A fellow prisoner, Douglas thought, and felt a renewed yearning for land under his feet and the fragrance of woods and flowers. Nothing grew on the surface of the sea.

In the days that followed, the horse's fitful cries were heard more and more often. Douglas tried to assist the

animal's owner but his knowledge of veterinary medicine
was limited. By the time Nantucket Shoals, with its
crowds of fishing vessels, came in sight, there appeared
to be no hope for the ailing horse. And when Cape Cod
appeared six leagues distant, on the twenty-seventh of
July, the horse's owner practically never left the animal's side. He had spent almost his entire savings in
buying passage for the animal and now it looked as if
he might as well have thrown his money into the sea.

On August 2, as Douglas stood gazing out at the
sandy, rock-stippled shores of Long Island, he heard
cries of dismay and excitement among the passengers.
Men and women were crowding around the owner of the
horse. One look at the man's trembling face and Douglas
knew that the horse was dead.

The death of the animal cast a pall over the ship and
over Douglas, in spite of his excitement over the end of
a fifty-nine-day journey. That night, as he saw the floating light at Sandy Hook, he thought of the plants that
he hoped to carry back to England with him. Plants, too,
could sicken and die. Collecting the specimens was only
part of the job.

Something brushed against his trouser leg. He looked
down and saw the dog he had made friends with, wag-
ging its stubby tail. He stroked the animal's head, re-

membering his promise to himself. Next time he journeyed anywhere, he would have a dog. A man needed a
companion, if he were going to spend much of his time
in wilderness areas. Not that this expedition would bring
him into true wilderness, but if this were a success, who
knew where he might be sent the next time? Wherever
it was, it would be far from the hills and glens of Scotland and the people he loved.

"A Scottish terrier," he murmured and then laughed
at himself for worrying about the need for company just
then. The ship was sailing toward the growing city of
New York where there were over a 100,000 people.

The dog trotted off and Douglas went to his cabin.

Hot August sunlight glazed the cobblestones and the
brick housefronts, and the masts of ships lying at anchor
in the East River. A sluggish breeze came off the Hudson
River on Manhattan Island's other side but it had no
effect on the ninety-six-degree heat that gripped the city.
Douglas, riding in a hired open carriage, looked with
envy at the women walking by, parasols giving them a
fragment of shade, at least. Men in high, black beaver
hats and black frock coats sought the shade of canvas
awnings. In the distance, a fat pig lay happily in a
gutter where a leaky wooden plug on a fire hydrant let

a trickle of water run down. As Douglas looked at the pig, a crowd of firemen passed by, pushing and pulling a rattling fire engine toward a plume of smoke drifting up from a roof a number of blocks beyond. The firemen's red shirts looked like bits of flame and Douglas mopped his brow, feeling scorched.

The carriage turned onto William Street, passing the North Dutch church, before turning again onto Fulton toward the market where Douglas wanted to inspect the vegetables so that he could report in detail to the Horti-cultural Society. The produce was lush—carrots, red onions, immense numbers of melons and cucumbers, apples, pears, some poorly ripened peaches, many kinds of squash, plums, and even pineapples and coconuts from the West Indies. The only thing that was lacking or poor in quality was cauliflower, he noted. In the inter-ests of his parched throat, rather than science, he bought one juicy pineapple and ate it on the spot before he went touring the city again.

He began to feel at home in New York City after days of exploring its streets by carriage or on foot. Not only the city but the countryside: the fine orchards on Long Island, the wonderful variety of soil and vegetation on Staten Island—oaks and maples, wild berry bushes, and many wild flowers. Thanks to Dr. David Hosack and

Thomas Hogg, New Yorkers interested in botany, he had seen much more of the city and its environs than he would have otherwise. It was saddening, however, to see the twenty acres of Hosack's Elgin Botanical Garden north of the city's outskirts, the first garden of its kind in New York, going to ruin for lack of public support. But there were fine old Dutch orchards across the Hudson.

"I notice," he said to Hosack one day, "that whenever a particularly fine product is grown or made in this country it is named George Washington, be it a plum or a fire engine."

Hosack smiled. "Not all," he said. "Some are named Martha Washington."

Hogg, who had a nursery at what is now Broadway and Twenty-third Street, took Douglas by steamer and stagecoach to Philadelphia. There, Douglas found that the gardens and trees were superior to those of New York and that the streets and houses of the Quaker city were far cleaner. The vegetables at Philadelphia's High Street market were the finest he had seen. Most interesting, though, were the collections of plant specimens brought back by Lewis and Clark, on display at various Philadelphia institutions.

As Douglas looked at the collections, he tried to visualize the wilderness from which they had come, his longing to visit those wild scenes growing stronger.

On September 4, after visiting more nurserymen and orchardists around New York, collecting specimens and cataloging them, Douglas set off by Hudson River steamboat for Albany, the capital of the state. At Albany he called on the former governor De Witt Clinton, who was a member of the Horticultural Society of London, and after a day's stay received advice about the rest of his journey.

From Albany he traveled through a downpour, by stagecoach, but the road was so rough that his bones felt as if they would be jolted from his body, and at Little Falls he changed to a canalboat on the Erie Canal. He arrived at Rochester where he took the stagecoach again. After more days of stagecoach travel and a steamship ride of sixty hours on Lake Erie, he was put on an island in the Detroit River to be rowed across the water to Amherstburg, in Canada. Douglas bundled his trunk into a birchbark canoe manned by an Indian, and settled down a bit nervously for his canoe journey toward the French-Canadian village beyond. His nervousness grew less as the canoe cut through the water swiftly and lightly and the farms and garrison of Amherstburg appeared on the farther shore. Beyond the farms and orchards the dark forest stood like a shaggy, blue-green shadow. A breeze whipping across the water brought the tangy scent of oak leaves and forest loam to his nostrils. He inhaled deeply, his eyes on the forest, the wild vegetation, and the birds skimming across the tree tops.

The trip was over all too quickly. On shore he received a warm handshake from Henry Briscoe, a friend of Joseph Sabine's brother. And in a few minutes, over food and a hot beverage, Briscoe suggested an outing to the forest east of town for the next day.

The next morning they set out with dogs and a gun. Briscoe, an excellent marksman, said when Douglas had hit a difficult target with the gun, "You've used one of these before, I see."

"Aye," Douglas said. "Shooting's a handy art."

"Especially if there are hostile Indians around."

"Or friendly acorns." Douglas drew a bead on a cluster of acorns growing on a giant oak. The gun barked and the bough from which the acorns hung snapped in the middle and came rattling down to earth. Douglas picked the branch up and deposited the specimen nuts in his bag along with seeds of asters, sunflowers, goldenrod, ironweed, and gentian.

That night, he wrote wearily but happily in his journal: "This is what I might term my first day in America."

In the days following, Douglas went off alone to explore the fields and woods, borrowing Briscoe's gun to
help add specimens to his collection. He made his way
to the neighboring rivers, too, collecting plants which
would one day bloom along the Thames in England. He
also took samples of Indian corn and tobacco from the
fields.

It was during a trip to Lake St. Clair, beyond the
French settlement of Sandwich, that Douglas found
America had unpleasant as well as pleasant surprises
to offer.

Hiring a guide and a hack, he set off one morning for
Lake St. Clair. The guide was a dark and restless individual who had little to say beyond barking French words
at the horse. Douglas gave up trying to talk and sat listening to the forest sounds, half-hoping that some wild
animal like a bear or a fox would show up. He saw nothing more exciting than the flashing red of a cardinal and
great flocks of pigeons, whose whirring wings sounded
like a rush of water.

At the end of the trail, the guide dismounted from
the hack, tethered the horse, and led the way toward the
oak forest which Douglas wanted to explore. The two
walked for five miles, Douglas stopping often along the
trail to gather plant specimens, each of which he placed

between botanical papers. This took time so that the sun was high when he and the guide reached a stand of giant black oaks whose splendor made Douglas catch his breath.

High above, fat acorns glittered temptingly. Douglas was without a gun with which to try shooting them down. He looked at one of the tallest trees a moment, then stripped off his coat, tossed it on a nearby branch, and approached the tree. This would not be the first time he had climbed after a prize, he thought, remembering the many Scottish trees and cliffs he had conquered.

As he climbed, hugging the trunk with his arms and legs, he felt joy in the venture and in his own wiry strength. Ten feet. Twenty. He was up among the shining leaves now, his hands and feet seeking for purchase on the heavy but branchless trunk. A squirrel scolded him and then went leaping past, one of the fat acorns in its teeth.

"What a botanist needs is a trained squirrel," Douglas said to himself. He reached a crotch in the oak some forty feet up, then made his way out along a limb to where acorns hung like ornaments of dull brass. He paid no attention to the guide below but concentrated on selecting the choicest seeds to cram into his pockets. Wait until Sabine and Hooker saw these beauties!

There. That was enough. Five minutes and he had a

golden-brown harvest. Glancing below, he saw his coat
move strangely on its branch support. Douglas thought
that the breeze had stirred it, when he saw the dark hand
of his guide jerk the coat completely free. Before Douglas could do more than blink, the guide had bundled the
coat under his arm and started toward the underbrush.

"What are—come back here!" Douglas shouted.

The man glanced upward, then began to run at top
speed.

Douglas slid down the trunk, scraping his hands and
shins. When he reached the ground he hurried in pursuit of the thief but the man had too good a start. Douglas panted to a stop, still incredulous. The guide had
been recommended to him in Sandwich. So much for
recommendations! So much for his one and only coat,
too, and for his small vasculum, his notes and receipts,
and his money. Nineteen dollars was not a fortune, perhaps, but it was a high price for a handful of acorns.
He wondered how he would explain the incident to the
Horticultural Society in London; they would expect a
full accounting of his expenses.

Well, there was nothing to be done about it except to
walk to the carriage and drive back to his lodging. He
tied the acorns carefully in his neckcloth and set out,
his face more flushed from anger than from heat. For
now, without his coat, the shadowy forest began to send

a chill around him. By the time he reached the horse and carriage, he was shivering. Wearily, he climbed up onto the seat, took the reins, and commanded the horse to start forward. The horse merely flicked its ears. Douglas tried again, touching the whip to the animal's rump, but with no more success. After several more attempts, he realized it was useless. The horse would not budge.

Douglas went on, on foot, ruefully wishing that Sabine had recommended that he study a little French along with his Spanish. But Sabine couldn't know that he was going to have dealings with a horse that understood only French!

He never saw either the guide or his property again and was forced to borrow a coat from a friendly settler to wear back to Sandwich.

Douglas continued his botanizing in the area, crossing the river to Michigan near the raw frontier town of Detroit. Toward the end of September he journeyed back toward New York, taking a three-day side-trip to Niagara Falls. Although he looked with the proper awe at the pounding geysers of water, his real interest was in the red cedars growing from the cliffs, and plants heavy with seed.

Back in Albany on October 8, he found the old Dutch city given over to bands, waving flags, and saluting guns as the town celebrated the opening of the east-

ern section of the Erie Canal. Douglas watched the cele-
bration from a distance, quietly unpacking his collections, arranging them and putting them in fresh folders.
He felt a deep, warm triumph as he surveyed his botanical treasures. They were compensation enough for the
aches and pains that had settled in his knees to give
him a twinge almost every time he took a step.

"Ordinary rheumatism, young man," ex-Governor
Clinton declared when Douglas called on him again.

"I'm getting old fast, it seems," Douglas said with
a wry smile.

In spite of his half-crippled legs, he took time to
spend a whole day at Albany looking for a species of
vegetation which he finally found in a ravine. Another
day was spent walking twelve miles in search of a certain
kind of herb, without success. When he finally left
Albany, he carried gifts from Clinton to Sabine: six
wild pigeons, boxes of fruit and minerals, books and
even moccasins.

The pain in his knees grew so keen that he could
scarcely walk. He was forced to rest for six days with
General Morgan Lewis at Clermont before going on.

Aching bones or weariness could not stop Douglas
long. He had a hundred things to do yet before he could

consider his job finished. There were more nurseries
to visit, more orchards and more wild forests. And
other important persons to see.

One of these was Thomas Nuttall, who had collected
on the Missouri River and in the Southwest. As Douglas
talked to the other botanist about his work, and about
his own, he felt freshly inspired. With Nuttall he visited
the John Bartram garden at Kingessing on the Schuylkill
River, the oldest botanical garden in America.

When Douglas finally returned to New York and got
ready to sail homeward, he found himself surrounded
by a mountain of specimens, notes, presents, birds, and
living plants which he must sort out and care for and
somehow manage to transport to England in good shape.
Fruit trees which he had dug up himself had to be
packed. Clinton's pigeons—plus wood ducks and quail
—had to be given proper cages and adequate food and
water. His field notes had to be put into shape.

Still, the mention of a new plant sent him out searching. He and his friend Hogg spent two days slogging
through mud and mire in a swamp across the Hudson.
Hogg, at one place, sank through to his waist. Douglas
thought of his rheumatic knees. It was scarcely helpful
treatment. But what did it matter when a few yards away
was a bright and beautiful pitcher plant sprouting from

the bog? Hogg felt the same way. Together, spattered with mud and water, he and Douglas floundered on, returning happily to their headquarters with the swamp trophies.

Douglas also bought some choice plants from merchants and orchard growers. One of his most prized purchases was the Oregon grape which had been brought back from the Far West by Lewis and Clark.

At last, in December, surrounded by crates and cages, trunks and boxes, Douglas set sail for home on the ship *Nimrod*. Although the wind sweeping over the ship was cold, he felt a warmth of gratitude for the friendship and hospitality he had received in America.

The trip back to England took only about half the time that the trip over had taken. The most seasick passengers were two of the wood ducks Douglas had brought. And instead of a horse, on this trip four pigeons died as a result of a fight that broke out in the pigeon cage.

Neither sick ducks nor dead pigeons dimmed the glory of Douglas' return, however. Said the official paper of the Horticultural Society: "This mission was executed by Mr. Douglas with a success beyond expectation. He obtained many plants which were much wanted, and greatly increased our collection of fruit trees by the acquisition of several sorts known only to us by name."

Success beyond expectation. Young Douglas, taking over his garden duties again, felt well-rewarded. Yet, even as he displayed his gleanings and shyly told of his experiences in the eastern United States, he was remembering the ride in the birchbark canoe, the great green-blue shadow of the forests, the lure of a further wilderness.

And he remembered something else, a promise he had made to himself.

It was Hooker, on a visit to London, who first saw Douglas' new and most surprising possession. Turning in at the gate of the Chiswick gardens, Hooker saw Douglas strolling outside the garden, a shaggy, bumbling terrier pup at his heels.

"What kind of botanical specimen is this?" Hooker asked, eyeing the furry bundle.

Douglas, smiling, said, "This is Billy, sir. The future companion of my travels."

"Indeed," said Hooker. "And where are you traveling to, Davy?"

Douglas picked the puppy up, snuggling him against his chest. "Somewhere, I don't doubt, sir."

Hooker, looking at his former student, the determined blue eyes, the steady chin, nodded slowly. "I don't doubt it, either, lad." He scratched Billy's ears. "You'll take care of him, won't you, Billy?"

"We've already promised to take care of each other," Douglas said with a grin. "And each remain single." He pushed at the gate. "I want to show you the beautiful trailing arbutus—*Epigaea repens,* that is—which I brought back." At that moment, Billy squirmed from Douglas' grasp and bounded to the ground. He went bouncing toward a bed of ice lettuce, his clumsy feet trampling the edge of the plants.

"Nay, Billy!" Douglas cried and raced after him.

Hooker leaned on his cane and laughed. "Your faithful companion hasn't yet learned the difference between a rare plant and weeds, I fear."

Douglas shook his head sadly as he gathered the dog up in his arms again. "In fact, I think he rather prefers weeds. Well, he's only a bairn yet."

Chapter Four

River of the West

On the northwestern edge of North America, thousands
of miles from Liverpool or even New York, a great river
thrashed its way from the Canadian wilderness southward and then westward toward the Pacific Ocean. It
filled the air with its white thunder. It lashed at its banks
and boiled into long, foaming rapids and whirling cascades. Near Indian villages it stormed in the channels
the Indians had dug to trap the bright salmon that each
year battled their way upstream.

The plains and forests and cliffs along the river
echoed its roar. But back from the river's shores, in
the thick stands of pine and fir and cedar, the silence
was so vast that even the cry of a lynx or the howl of a
timber wolf seemed mere scratches of sound, the silence
flowing in around these like another kind of river. There,

51

grizzlies and elk followed their old trails; coyotes and
mountain lions; mule deer and beavers. Over the trails of
the animals came the Indians: Chinook and Tillamook,
Nez Percé and Cayuse. Over the Indian trails, finally,
came the white man.

The Indians called the two-thousand-mile river the
Ouragon or Oregon, and so the area around, from
British-claimed land in the north to the Spanish southwest, and between the Rocky Mountains and the Pacific,
was named the Oregon Territory. To the white men the
river was known as the Columbia.

In April, 1825, nearly two years after his trip to
eastern America, David Douglas arrived at the mouth
of the Columbia in a ship belonging to the Hudson's
Bay Company, the *William and Ann*. For six windy,
rain-beaten weeks the ship had been forced to stay outside the channel entrance, waiting for calmer weather.
It had anchored first in Baker's Bay, inside the treacherous sandbar that stretched across the river's mouth,
before coming on to Forth George. It now rocked lan-
guidly between the stockaded and bastioned assembly of
buildings that was the fort, and a cluster of rush-mat
huts that was a Chinook village.

On board, Douglas straightened from helping crew
members and one of the Company's clerks, young
Alexander McKenzie, load his trunks into a wooden

canoe. Douglas' face was even ruddier than usual, from sun and wind. Salt spray had matted his curling hair. But already his hands were streaked with the green juice of vegetation, for while the ship stood at anchor in Baker's Bay he had managed to go ashore on Cape Disappointment. He and John Scouler, who had been appointed surgeon-naturalist to the *William and Ann*, had raced from one plant to another, like two-legged bees.

Now, Scouler looked at Douglas' trunks and shook his head. "You've enough baggage, Douglas, to start a settlement of your own."

"Aye, and I'll need it all; a hundred cases and crates couldn't contain all the seeds and plants I expect to find here. I want them ready to ship back to England by the time the ship leaves this fall." His gaze lingered on Scouler. Added to his joy in being appointed for this trip had been the joy of finding his former classmate on board with him. "I wish you could stay on with me, John. We'd have a green feast."

Scouler nodded, then smiled in the direction of a small gray terrier who was standing spraddle-legged, short tail waving, while he barked at an Indian canoe approaching the vessel. "You'll have Billy for company."

Douglas called the dog to his side. "Hear how he

talks back to the Indians? He's learning the language so he can be my interpreter. Isn't that the truth, Billy Boy?"

Billy whined, squeaked, and barked.

"That's Chinook right enough," Scouler said. "Here they come. The captain's letting them on board. Get ready to barter. The captain says they have their burial canoes up river on some rock. I'd like to take a few skulls and bones back in my collection."

"You might be risking your own bones if you try that, John. Those burial grounds are sacred—" He broke off, staring at the savage walking toward them.

Scouler stared, too. Billy took a step backward, getting behind the shelter of one of Douglas' legs while he peered at the approaching Indian.

The Indian was old. His face was wrinkled, and one eye looked toward them sightlessly. The other eye was alert and appraising. Douglas and Scouler had got over their first surprise at seeing the men and women of the tribes along the shore going half-naked—the women wore a cedar-string skirt and the men a fur blanket draped over their shoulders. But this red man was dressed in an old English lace-decked coat, breeches, and a cocked hat. Hanging clumsily from his waist was a sword. And fluttering proudly from one threadbare lapel was a faded remnant of the British flag.

Behind Douglas, Captain Hanwell whispered, "Chief Concomly."

With dignity, Chief Concomly stopped and raised his hand. "How are you, men of King George? We welcome King George man. All here King George's men together." He saw Billy out of the corner of his one good eye. "We welcome King George dog. Our dogs also good King George men."

Douglas, trying to conceal his amusement, murmured what he hoped was an appropriate reply, and glanced toward Captain Hanwell for assistance. Help arrived in the form of the chief trader, Donald Manson. Manson started a conversation with Concomly and the other Indians crowding around, in a language that was a mixture of the Chinook's own tongue, scraps of English, and much sign language.

"The chief says," Manson interpreted, "that Mr. Douglas and Mr. Scouler are welcome to his lodge and that his people will exchange much fish and berries for beads, knives, or other goods."

One of the Indians, a squat, plump fellow with a copper disk hanging from his pierced nostrils, stood eyeing Billy. "Much fat dog," he said.

Douglas picked Billy up, recalling that he had been told that dogs were considered tasty eating by many Indians.

"Much fat Indian," Douglas said bluntly, eyeing the Chinook in turn.

Chief Concomly's good eye twinkled. He grinned toothlessly. In a moment, the plump Indian was being pointed at by his fellows as they grinned and laughed, jumping around the victim of Douglas' humor. The only one who was not pleased was the plump man himself, who began talking rapidly in Chinook, and making threatening gestures toward Douglas.

Concomly said something to the Indian, calling him "Amaham," and he slunk off.

When he had a chance, Douglas inquired about Concomly's costume. Manson told him that the old chief had received the clothes from a former sea captain long ago and that the costume was his proudest possession.

"He is a good chief," Manson went on. "A great help to us here. And to Dr. McLoughlin, the Chief Factor. I'm expecting McLoughlin tomorrow or the next day, from Fort Vancouver. I sent one of the lads to him, telling him of your arrival. Now, if you want to come ashore with your trunks, Mister Douglas, you're welcome to sup with us. And Mister Scouler here, as well."

The two accepted, for there were still several hours of daylight left and Scouler was as eager as Douglas to continue explorations on shore. Billy, too, took his place in the canoe. The Indians, constantly curious, brought their own canoes alongside, so that there was a small armada as the group set out from the ship.

Douglas looked seaward, remembering the three species of trees he had seen when the ship had rounded the point before reaching Cape Disappointment. A hemlock, a balsam fir, and a species he was uncertain of. The species which he could not name was the one which interested him most. He looked at the trees growing nearer at hand in the vicinity of the fort.

There it was! The same kind of tree! Dark and towering it pricked the gray-blue sky, its flat, dark green needles glistening, its many cones drooping from its evenly spaced branches. A giant going straight up and up like the mast of some mighty ship, but a mast crowned with fragrant plumes. A *Pinus taxifolia*, perhaps? The surgeon-naturalist, Archibald Menzies, had brought twig specimens of that species to England in 1795, but no seeds or cone specimens had been obtained.

Douglas listened to the slapping sound of water against the canoe prows, breathing in the air that carried the scent of campfires and warm earth and the sea. At last he was where he wanted to be, after eight months on shipboard. His spirits felt as high as the tip of the great fir he had marveled at. Never before had a botanist set foot in this wilderness. Everywhere around him lay unimaginable treasures, only waiting for him to find them.

Stroking Billy's head, he added mentally: dangers and hazards, too. Perhaps he had spoken too quickly to the fat Indian, for instance. The savages seemed docile enough, thanks to the restraining influence of the Hudson's Bay men. But without the help of a common language or common traditions, it would be easy to make a mistake.

A memory of his brother John's tearful face as he and Douglas had parted on the dock at Liverpool returned to him. His own eyes had not been dry. And when he had stood on the deck looking back at the rocky shores of Cornwall, red with the long rays of the setting sun, he had thought it might be the last time he would ever look at England's shores. Of the last three collectors the Horticultural Society had sent out to remote regions, one had died in Africa, another had become ill during explorations in Bengal and China and had died on his return. One had survived. It was not an encouraging record.

Among the supplies and scientific equipment in his

trunk was the Bible that an old friend at Scone, Mr.
Scott, had given him long ago. "There, David," Mr. Scott
had said, "I cannot recommend a better or more important book for your perusal."

Certainly he had been favored so far and he felt a
humble gratitude toward the Supreme Power that had
given him so much so soon. Here he was, only twenty-six
years old, and already he had seen more of the world
than most men see in a lifetime. On the journey, stops
had been made at Madeira, Rio de Janeiro, Cape Horn,
Juan Fernandez Island off the coast of Chile, and James
Island in the Galapagos group. From a distance he had
seen the coasts of Mexico and California. During his
stops he had jammed his collecting cases with seeds and
plants so that already there were treasures aboard the
William and Ann. He and Scouler had turned the ship
into a floating laboratory.

The sound of the canoe's prow lightly touching land
jerked him back to the present. He sprang ashore,
Scouler with him, Billy eagerly leaping ahead. Trusting
his trunks and other cargo to the chief trader, Douglas
set off with his friend for a trip through the woods.

Just ahead was shrub after shrub of salal, the first
exciting plant he and Scouler had seen when they had
explored the cape. Now he saw salmonberry and red

currant, rhododendron and wild grape with its leaves like holly. Everywhere some new bloom or bud beckoned.

He paused an instant, overwhelmed. Billy stopped at his heels, looking up with inquiring eyes.

"Too much—too much—" Douglas choked.

Billy barked softly, and Douglas pulled his shaggy companion close. "It's not only Chinook you understand, laddie, but my foolish stammerings, too."

He caught a glimpse of a strange yellow bloom freckled with maroon poking out from a shady nook, but when he began to look for it, he could not find it. In his excitement and over-eagerness, he wandered in wider and wider circles.

"Look here," Scouler called to him. "Isn't this a species of *mimulus*, Douglas?"

"That's it! What I was searching for." Douglas joined his friend and stooped down, his face close to the impish-looking bloom. "And here it was, right under my nose."

"Under *my* nose, you mean," Scouler laughed, and quoted with a broad accent an old Scotch saying: " 'Ye gae far about seeking the nearest, mon.' "

"Aye," Douglas admitted. He picked the yellow bloom, dreaming of it flickering like a tiny lamp in some far-off English garden in the years to come. *Mimulus moschatus,* the musk-scented monkey flower.

He got up, already looking around for a new species,
his mind now leaping ahead of him eagerly. But he forced
himself to move slowly and search each spot thoroughly
before going on to the next.

The evening of the following day, Chief Factor Mc-
Loughlin arrived. McLoughlin, at forty, was a tall,
rugged man with white hair hanging to his shoulders. He
arrived in a canoe manned by Indians and a Canadian.

As Douglas walked toward him, he felt all of his old
shyness and nervousness arise. It had taken only a few
hours at Fort George to realize that John McLoughlin
was the most important man in this wilderness. He was
called "Doctor" because he had once studied medicine
in Canada before switching to the fur trade. It was only
recently that McLoughlin had been named Chief Factor
of the Columbia River district for the Hudson's Bay
Company, but already he had started building the new
fur trading post, Fort Vancouver, ninety miles from the
Columbia's mouth.

The Indians called McLoughlin "The White-headed
Eagle." Douglas felt his own stature diminish, confronted with the other's six-foot-four-inch height. Then,
as McLoughlin took his hand, smiled, and said in his
thickly burred, slightly jerky voice, "We're honored,

indeed, to have a plant collector from the Horticultural Society here with us, Mister Douglas," his discomfiture vanished. There was no mistaking the sincerity and friendliness in the tall man's voice.

Scouler received the same warm welcome. Douglas showed the Chief Factor his written instructions from the Society and explained in detail the object of his visit.

"Now, Douglas," McLoughlin said at last, "you must move your supplies to Fort Vancouver and be my guest there. This is all but abandoned here. You can eat at my table and share what there is to share, and I will do all in my power to promote your work. One thing I don't have to offer is a roof. My own is not ready. But if you don't mind starting out with a tent—"

"A tent in this world would be a castle," Douglas said.

McLoughlin nodded, studying Douglas. "Aye!" His gaze went to the broad sweep of the Columbia and Douglas saw more than ambition or authority in the man's face. The look he gave the river was one of love. "We'll plan to start tomorrow morning. You can take a few supplies with you but the bulk will have to be sent up later. Now, if you'll excuse me while I go talk to the captain—"

"Tomorrow," Douglas said to Scouler as McLoughlin left. "That means I'll be leaving you here."

"The ship has most of its supplies still on board," Scouler answered. "Perhaps, while the unloading's going on, I can take a trip up river and visit you." He turned suddenly. "Ah, there's your good friend 'Much-Fat' prowling around, giving you the evil eye."

Douglas sent the nearby Indian a glance, then looked quickly for Billy. The terrier was sleeping peacefully in the shade of an Indian dugout hauled up on shore. With another glance at the fat Indian who was dividing his time between watching Douglas and scratching at fleas on his arms and thighs, Douglas took his pipe from its pouch, tamped tobacco into it, and then found the small magnifying glass he carried with him. Putting the pipe in his mouth, he held the lens over it so that the sun shone in one concentrated ray on the tobacco. In a few moments, the sun's heat began its work. A tendril of smoke twisted upward from the tobacco. Douglas sucked on the pipe's stem, helping the sun do its job. There! The pipe was lighted; a billow of smoke puffed up from the bowl.

From the corner of his eye he saw Much-Fat clap his hand over his mouth in a gesture of astonishment and dread.

"Ecutoh! Olla-piska!" the Indian exclaimed behind his hand, then turned and waddled off toward some of his comrades in the distance.

"Whatever he said," Scouler commented, "I believe your little trick had the right effect."

"I have a feeling I may need more than one trick in my bag," Douglas said, calling Billy to his side. "I won't always have a Hudson's Bay Company's fort at my back."

That evening he told Dr. McLoughlin what the Indian had said.

McLoughlin translated. "The Indian said you were a bad spirit, Douglas. A man of fire."

Douglas could not help smiling to himself. A man of fire and a bad spirit! This was a new role for him.

Chapter Five

Wilderness Walker

For the first hour of his trip up the Columbia, Douglas' attention was fixed on the canoe itself and on the boat-men. The Canadian serving as steersman stood in the stern of the twenty-five-foot craft, governing the canoe's path by deft manipulatioins of his long paddle. On narrow seats hung from the gunwales, five Indians sat in a double row, stroking their shorter paddles in a steady, constant rhythm, while the sixth sat in the bow. On two of the seats sat Douglas and McLoughlin. Billy lay at Douglas' feet. The cargo was stored near the stern and covered with oilcloth.

This canoe, McLoughlin had explained, was of the kind used by the voyageurs, those specialized French-Canadian canoemen of the rivers and streams throughout the north. Made of yellow birchbark, light enough for

65

the boatmen to carry it over portages, it could hold three-
thousand pounds besides the crew. The *canot du nord*,
McLoughlin had called it. The canoe of the north.

The Indian canoes, Douglas had observed, were
usually hollowed out by fire and stone axes from large
cedar trees. Most had high, carved prows. Skimming
over the water, the large canoes looked surprisingly light
under the skilful handling of the natives. These Indians
were extremely dirty, and grotesque by white men's
standards, with their artificially flattened heads. They
had a long reputation for thievery as well. Yet Douglas'
chagrin and disappointment—he had expected tall, dig-
nified, noble savages—was tinged with admiration. With
a minimum of tools, the Indians had developed a way of
life that suited their surroundings, using the materials
at hand. They did not seem bloodthirsty, either. Still,
it would not be wise to be careless.

He turned from thoughts of the Indians and the
canoe to the river's green shores, longing to feel the
earth under his feet again. Once established at Fort
Vancouver, he would be able to take to the trails with
Billy, independent of canoes and ships, his vasculum on
his back. One of his first tasks would be to collect seeds
from the giant fir he called *Pinus taxifolia*. As the canoe
cut the water southeastward, he saw more and more of

the great, soaring trees. Their cones, shining far up at
the top of the tall trunks, looked impossibly remote. The
chances of being able to shoot them down with buckshot
were slim. And he could scarcely hope to fell one of the
giants with his hatchet. As for climbing—he remembered the guide back at Amherstburg who had run off
with all of his belongings. But somehow he would get
the cones, even if he had to invent a pair of wings.

Billy whined restlessly at his feet. Both he and Douglas
were cramped into a small space. McLoughlin, Douglas
saw, sat with his long legs doubled up under him. The
few voyageurs Douglas had seen, including the steersman behind him, were small men, big in the shoulders
and chest, light and narrow in the legs.

Looking down at his booted feet, he felt a slight chill
as he thought how easily one could shove a foot through
the brittle bark and let in the cold water below.

This close to the sea, the river was influenced by the
tides. Now, with the tide going out and current and wind
against them, the oarsmen's muscles tensed with the
fight against the river.

McLoughlin, seated in front of Douglas, called back
the names of spots of interest. Tongue's Point—Oathla-
muck Point—and an Indian village whose name Douglas
could not catch because of the wind. He tried to mem-

orize the landmarks and names for future reference, noting the type of vegetation growing near each. On both sides of the river, thick forests came to the water's edge.

On and on the canoe went, the Indians paddling tirelessly, the steersman occasionally bellowing an order in French or Chinook, whichever mood he was in. The party stopped briefly at noon, for food and rest on shore, though the Indians ate nothing but a few salmonberry shoots.

Douglas, eager to be on the way again, ate lightly too, of the dried salmon and bread in McLoughlin's hamper. Back in the canoe, he watched the trees and the sky and the curves of the river with great interest. Billy, snuggled against him, slept.

"Here's Puget's Island," McLoughlin called back. "Keep a sharp lookout, Douglas, and you may soon see something to interest you, though it might interest Scouler more."

Once past the island, the rocks in the river became higher. The sun was slanting at a low angle when Douglas spotted one isolated cliff on the north bank of the river. Its crest appeared crowded with objects that looked oddly like Indian canoes supported on scaffolds. He squinted against the glare of the water. Billy sat up and barked.

McLoughlin answered the question Douglas did not ask. "One of the Chinook burial grounds," he said.

As the canoe swept past the citadel of rock, Douglas stared. There must be two or three hundred canoes! One, on a lower ledge, revealed its cargo—human bones carefully wrapped in a matting of rushes. But the rushes had decayed under the long rains and suns, and the bones gleamed. Pots and pans and baskets were crowded into the canoe with the dead owner's paddle, bow and arrow, and spear. Ornaments of shells and beads lined the canoe's interior and were even stuffed into the skull where there had once been a mouth.

Billy's bark changed to a howl and one of the Indian oarsmen broke his rhythm long enough to send an accusing glance at the excited terrier.

"Whist, Billy!" Douglas clamped his hand around the dog's muzzle. McLoughlin, he noticed, kept sternly silent out of respect for the Indians' dead.

With the sun's red rays lighting up the nearby landscape and the distant peaks of mountains, the scene lost some of the peaceful beauty it had held and took on an atmosphere of faint menace. Fog gathered along the shore and mist mixed with the foam of the river, adding to the chill that sent a slight shiver along Douglas' spine. It was not a shiver of fear so much as a shiver of wonder. What was he doing here, a stranger in a distant land with only the unfamiliar figure of a fur trader between him and the wilderness?

His fingers closed on Billy's warm fur, the only bit of Scotland he could feel and touch. Billy responded by running a very wet tongue against his master's wrist.

Darkness came like another kind of mist, velvety and moonless. McLoughlin ordered the canoe ashore for the night, and later Douglas stretched out gratefully beneath the overturned canoe with the Chief Factor, his stomach full of food and hot tea, Billy using his feet for a pillow.

"The ground is a hard mattress," McLoughlin murmured, "but I hope you will sleep well, Mister Douglas."

"I have slept on the ground before," Douglas said. He added, "But not with savages having a feast only a few steps away."

For the Indians were at last going to eat in earnest. They had caught a twenty-six pound sturgeon and were busily digging a pit in which to roast it.

Douglas struggled to keep his eyes open; it was not every night he had a chance to watch American red men from such a vantage point. In spite of himself, his aching eyes closed.

It was still dark when the canoe set off again. It stayed dark and gloomy even after the sun rose, for a thick cloud cover mantled the sky. Winter and early

spring brought heavy rains to the region, swelling the
Columbia and often causing floods.

Even in the gloom, the countryside impressed Douglas. He liked the rolling hills, the woods, the occasional
islands and Indian villages they passed as they traveled.
Many of the natives were preparing for the summer fishing season, the squaws busy making mats and baskets,
collecting plant roots for eating, and gathering shrubs.
The men worked at their nets, ropes, and spears. At one
camp, the whole tribe was enjoying itself, circles of men
and women gambling with polished discs or beaver-teeth
dice. Naked Indian children played in the water near
shore, or practiced shooting arrows from their bows.

And always, new kinds of vegetation beckoned from
the shores, some flowers just making their spring appear-
ance, others budding, still others in bloom: lupine,
pentstemon, evening primrose, hyacinths, grape, honey-
suckle, and many berry bushes. The summer would be
all too short, Douglas thought. Like a bee, he would have
to gather his loot chiefly when the plants were in bloom
or the seeds ripe.

The closer the canoe came to Fort Vancouver the more
splendid became the scenery. In the distance were the
snow-swept peaks of Mt. Hood, Mt. Jefferson and St.
Helens. Nearer at hand, blossoming meadows showed

among the forests, and fertile plains covered by deep
grass. Along the river, banks of limestone and blue
granite soared to several hundred feet high, sometimes
silvered by waterfalls.

When they reached Fort Vancouver, full night had
come, shrouding the unfinished buildings and the land.
The canoe turned toward the north bank and the steersman hailed those on shore.

As Douglas got out of the canoe, stiff-legged and
weary, he found himself the center of a group of curious
Indians. Two of the boatmen had just lifted one of
Douglas' trunks and his tin collecting box ashore.

In the flickering light of a pine torch held by one of
the Company's employees, Douglas saw an Indian with a
strangely twisted face working at the metal lid of the
vasculum in which Douglas had a number of plants.

He strode toward the man and wrenched the vasculum
from his grasp. The Indian gave a howl of pain. He had
got his fingertips under the lid and when Douglas seized
the box, the metal edge had caught the Indian's flesh.
He pulled his fingers free and stood sucking them, glowering at Douglas.

McLoughlin said something in Chinook and the Indian
retreated. With an air of apology, the Chief Factor
turned to Douglas. "You'll have to watch everything, all

the time. Be firm—try to be just—and have patience. They'll ask you a thousand questions, whether you understand or not. And they'll pry into every corner of your possessions they dare to. I'll help you find a guide —you'll need someone to accompany you, at first at any rate. But that can wait. You'll want to rest a few days, I daresay."

"Rest?" Douglas exclaimed, keeping his vasculum locked under his arm. "If I could see to collect, I'd start out now. I've no fear of getting lost. I have to learn my way alone sooner or later."

"It's not just a matter of getting lost," McLoughlin said. He looked at Douglas, his white hair shining in the orange glow of the torch. "Men have been murdered here, you know."

Douglas glanced apprehensively toward the Indian with the twisted face who was standing in shadow, still glowering.

McLoughlin added, "Tamto's harmless enough. Don't let his looks frighten you."

"What's wrong with his face?" Douglas asked.

"An unfortunate encounter with a black bear. Tamto was lucky to be left with a face at all. Now he's bear-shy. If there's one ten miles away, he seems to know it."

"Are there any grizzlies right around here?" Douglas asked.

"Aye. Just a week ago—"

There was a rustling in the brush behind Douglas. He wheeled. A furry creature emerged, eyes gleaming in the uncertain light. Douglas took a step backward before he saw that it was only Billy.

There was a high, tittering sound which seemed to come from the spot where Tamto stood. Douglas peered at the Indian. Although there was no change of expression on his face—perhaps there could not be on account of the scars—the Indian was definitely laughing at him.

Douglas' cheeks grew warm. He had never liked being laughed at.

"Usually," Dr. McLoughlin continued, "grizzlies won't bother you if you don't bother them. They don't come leaping out of the bushes, I can assure you." There was an unmistakable twinkle in the doctor's eye.

Suddenly, Douglas felt an answering twinkle of humor in himself. He—*Olla-piska,* the man of fire—had been frightened by his own pet dog! He walked toward the smirking Tamto and held out a twist of tobacco. "Here," he said. "For you. We laugh together."

Tamto hesitated, eyeing Douglas suspiciously. Then one unwashed hand darted out, seizing the tobacco before he ran off.

Douglas fastened a thin rope to Billy's collar. "Come along now, Grizzly. You all but wrecked my reputation here for good."

The sky above the Cascade range was a pale violet, scarcely touched by sunrise, when Douglas arose. Quietly, efficiently, he gathered his supplies, some biscuits and tea, and set off, tiptoeing as he passed a group of rush huts where loud snores told him the Indians were still asleep. With dawn he felt no fear of savages or grizzlies, and he did feel a need to be alone for his first real meeting with the region. However, he did not neglect to take his gun. He might come upon birds or game that he could take either for specimens or as food to contribute to the fort's larder.

Billy trotted at his heels, freed from the rope leash now, and as full of curiosity and energy as his master.

Together they followed the winding trails through a silence that deepened with every step. At a turn in the trail, a black-tailed deer confronted Douglas, its great eyes staring into his an instant before it made a leap into the shrubbery. Where the trail approached the river, a fisher, lithe and sleek, streaked along a fallen tree trunk. Ground squirrels darted in and out through the ground cover—a large tree squirrel scolded from a bough above. Once, Douglas paused to investigate a flat, long-clawed track. It looked like a bear track. When, a short distance ahead, he saw a tree bearing the marks of bear claws, he felt a small thrill.

"Stay close, lad," he admonished Billy.

The sun rose above the mountains, bringing light and warmth to the dim trails. Another hour, and perspiration speckled Douglas' forehead. Here and there swarms of gnats and mosquitoes filled the air, but he paid little attention. For there, on the right, was a starflower with its thin leaves spread out close to the earth, its dainty stem promising a fat bud. And there on the left a kind of barberry he had not seen before. And always, towering green and silver and blue-gray against the quickening bronze color of the sky, the great trees.

Noon came and Douglas built a small fire to make himself a basin of tea. He shot a couple of squirrels for Billy, then they went on.

Mile after mile he traveled, using the river as his chief compass. Occasionally, curious Indians appeared and followed at his side, asking questions in their strange language. The sounds were blends of grunts and coughs, whines and growls, all seemingly produced straight from their throats without using their tongues or lips. Douglas answered as well as he could in sign language, or with grunts of his own, together with nods and shakes of his head. He wondered if he would ever learn the language well enough to converse with these people.

In one place he met a squaw carrying a baby. The baby's head was being firmly pressed into the desired flattened and wedge-like shape by a board strapped against the forehead. The small black eyes seemed to bulge with the pressure but the child cooed merrily.

Several times the natives became too bold. One ventured to try to twist the metal buttons off Douglas' jacket and Douglas had to resort to his man-of-fire role, lighting his pipe with his lens.

He accidentally discovered still another means of gaining respect. When he was finally headed homeward, two squat Indian men trotting uncomfortably close beside him while they kept pointing at and fingering his vasculum, he found that the sun was directly in his eyes. He took his blue-tinted spectacles from their case and put them on.

The two Chinooks gasped, drew back, and clapped their hands over their mouths, horror and astonishment on their faces. As if hypnotized, they backed away into the dusky shadows, Billy foolishly trotting after them.

The braver of the two Indians lashed out with his foot, catching Billy's chin; the terrier came yelping back to Douglas for sympathy and protection.

"There's but one thing to do, Billy," Douglas said as he soothed the dog, "and that's to get you a pair of spectacles, too."

Tired, dirty, and hungry, he arrived back at the fort just in time to be invited to McLoughlin's table. During the meal he kept mentioning his intention of getting seeds from the coniferous tree that had impressed him.

"I must get a good specimen of the *Pinus taxifolia*," he said several times. "There'll be a problem getting the seeds, but there must be a way."

Sometime later, sitting near some of the company clerks who were entertaining themselves with a weird musical duet of bagpipes and a hoarse-sounding violin, he realized that Tamto was standing near and talking to several Indian cronies.

"I must find the *Pinus taxifolia*," he heard Tamto say with an air of great self-importance, in almost an exact copy of Douglas' own voice.

"Who him?" a comrade asked.

"Big chief," Tamto replied.

The wail of the bagpipes drowned out Douglas' laughter. I'll have to take Tamto on as a botanist-apprentice, he thought.

Douglas' rambles along the Columbia on his first day were relaxing strolls compared to the trips he made in the

days following. Up and down the river he went, climbing
slopes and scrambling into ravines, wading through
marshes and trudging across the hot, sandy plains of the
interior, until, as he noted in his journal, his feet were
"all one blister." While the *William and Ann* was still
in the harbor, John Scouler came up river and joined
Douglas in several trips in the fort's vicinity. On one of
their trips, to Menzies Island opposite the fort, Douglas
found a species of forget-me-not which both men agreed
should be named after their former teacher, William
Hooker.

When fur brigades set out from the fort, the canoes
loaded with beaver and otter skins that the Indians had
traded for buttons and beads, or that the Company's
trappers had collected, Douglas went along. On such
trips, he slept under an overturned canoe with the voyageurs. On other trips, he took a guide. Most often he
went alone with only Billy for company. If it was possible, he carried a tent. If not, he rolled himself in a
blanket and slept on a bed of pine boughs.

In heavy fogs, burning sun, or beating rains, he went,
always adding something new to his collection. Bird
specimens, too, found their way into his growing accu-
mulation: eagles, turkey buzzards, wild ducks, geese,
cormorants, herons, pigeons.

The early summer rains hindered his work more than

the constantly prying and pestering Indians did. Often Douglas got soaked while his jacket was wrapped around the plants to keep them dry. At the fort, he moved from his tent into a deerskin lodge but the dampness of his leather roof made the drying of his specimens difficult. And, in a very short time, the lodge was bulging with his collections so that there was scarcely room for anything else. Finally, a cedar-bark hut was built for him and his collections, and he moved into that on the rare occasions when he was not bedded down under a pine.

He often had to spend an hour drying his blanket before an open fire before he could settle down to rest. Aside from the few staples he carried, he lived off the land, shooting game for himself and Billy, or catching fish.

He took longer and longer trips, going with only an Indian boatman as far as Celilo Falls, some seventy miles from the fort. The Indians there and around the narrow, rock-studded channel called The Dalles had been very hostile a few years before, pillaging and killing white visitors. Douglas was the first white man to make the trip there and back without an armed guard. His tricks still held him in good stead, together with his growing understanding of the Indians. His reputation as a man of fire was helped by drinking "boiling water"—water

with an effervescent medicine in it. And the natives
began to understand that this roving gleaner of plants
came in peace. Some even brought him plant specimens
and seeds which they knew he wanted. Douglas repaid
them with the trinkets and merchandise which they
valued, or with tobacco, which served as currency. His
reputation spread from camp to camp. Slowly the Indians
began to give him yet another name, a name that pleased
Douglas more than any other title he had yet received.
They spoke of him as "The Grass Man."

Magic, or peaceful intentions did not always guarantee
his safety, however. Sometimes Douglas' real abilities
were put to the test, as during a visit to the village of
Chief Cockqua, a principal chief of the Chinooks near
the coast.

Douglas had made a laborious trip to the ocean to
search for certain roots along the shore of Cape Disappointment. Although he was told that the roots were
abundant around Point Adams, he did not dare go there
as the tribes of that region were at war. Setting out for
the trip back to Fort Vancouver, he stopped to visit Cockqua, only to discover that Cockqua's tribe and the Clat-
sops across the river were on very unfriendly terms.
Cockqua expected an attack on his village that very
night.

"You, *clachouie*," Cockqua said, using the word for "friend," "sleep with me in my lodge. There you be more safe from Clatsop warriors."

Douglas' tent had been brought within fifty yards of the Indian village. He looked at it, then at the cedar-bark lodge of the chief, feeling the eyes of the tribesmen upon him. If he boldly slept in his tent, acting as if he had no fear of the other tribe, these Indians would be deeply impressed by his courage.

As he wondered whether he did have the courage to sleep in the path of possible yelling warriors, he observed Cockqua scratching mightily at his red-brown belly. Fleas, too, were guests of the chief!

Douglas peaked his fingers to resemble the peak of his tent. "A chief of King George has no fear of the Clatsop," he said in stammering Chinook. "I sleep in my own house which I brought with me." He patted his rifle to show he had protection.

There were murmurs of admiration. One squat Chinook, however, said, "Clatsop shoot much good. I, Wanapah—" he prodded his own chest with his index finger, "also good shooter. When sun comes again, I show. Then you show."

Douglas understood that he was being challenged to a duel in marksmanship in the morning. He nodded, trying to maintain his look of confidence. Inwardly, he was full

of doubt as he followed Cockqua to a canoe where a giant
ten-foot sturgeon lay.

"Pickem part of fish you want," Cockqua offered.
"Then we roast him fine."

Douglas indicated that he liked the flesh near the head
and Cockqua ordered a slave, a browbeaten Indian from
a tribe who had been beaten in battle, to cut off the
chosen part.

While Douglas and the chief waited for the feast,
they passed the chief's pipe back and forth and tried to
talk to each other. Douglas openly admired the chief's
hat, an ingenious creation of cedar bark ornamented by
beargrass.

Cockqua explained that the hat had been made by a
young relative, a twelve-year-old girl, and that he would
present it to Douglas as a gift. He promised, too: "She
will make hats for you like the ones on the heads of the
chiefs of King George."

Douglas expressed his appreciation, then went on to
mention his desire for some ripe seeds of a certain kind
of blueberry in the area. The seeds he had obtained were
still green.

When the squaws announced that the sturgeon was
ready, Douglas took his portion of the fish and ate with
relish. He was very hungry.

Later, when warriors whooped their way through a

war dance, their paint-daubed faces shining in the light of the fires, their weapons glinting, he wondered if fleas and a diminished reputation might not have been the better part of valor. The war chants still echoing in his ears, he finally stretched out in his lonely tent, Billy at his feet. He had not entirely escaped from the friendly fleas. Both he and Billy scratched regularly while Douglas kept his ears tuned for the first war whoop from the tribe on the other side of the water. Whether the hostile Indians attacked or not, he felt it would be wise to be on the alert, his gun loaded, his eyes and ears open.

"A sleeping cat makes a proud mouse," he murmured to Billy. "We'd better watch this mousehole and be ready."

As midnight came without any sight or sound of attack, his eyelids drooped and he fell asleep. The next thing he knew, the sun was shining through the cracks of his tent and Billy was licking his face.

Douglas sat up, trying to rub away the haze of slumber and fatigue. Unless the Indian marksman, Wanapah, was a mere braggart, he would need keen sight this morning.

It took only a few minutes of watching Wanapah display his skill for Douglas to know that the Indian was an expert with his bow and arrow. As another Indian tossed a hoop of grass high into the air, Wanapah sighted along his arrow, shot, and sent the shaft through the hoop's center. After the shot he looked toward Douglas with glittering self-satisfaction.

Douglas waited while Wanapah went on to demonstrate his skill with a rifle. With this he placed a ball of shot within an inch of a mark set up 110 yards away.

Finally, he swaggered up to Douglas. "No chief of King George can shoot like Wanapah! Is it not so? Nor can the white chiefs dance the war dance nor sing the death song. Now, you shoot."

"This chief of King George," Douglas said calmly, "does not shoot at targets which sit still." He had observed that these Indians never tried to bring down birds on the wing but crept up on sitting targets. On a distant stump sat a white-headed eagle which the Indians called a "chuck-chuck," its plumage ruffled by the wind coming across the water. Douglas charged his gun with small swan shot, then walked within forty-five yards of the bird. He picked up a stone and flung it.

The stone clipped the eagle's tail. With a screech, the bird left the stump, wings beating. Douglas sighted as the eagle flew upward. He pressed the trigger. The eagle gave another squawk—its last—and tumbled to the earth. Douglas walked to where the bird lay, picked it up, and returned with it to toss it at Wanapah's feet.

Wanapah stood with his hand clapped over his mouth. All the others—squaws, slaves, and the bold, would-be warriors of the night before—did the same. Even Chief Cockqua pressed his hand to his mouth.

Wanapah, however, recovered to challenge Douglas' marksmanship once more. "Me make eagle of hat." He tapped the grass hat on his long, black hair, then removed it, indicating that he would toss it into the air as a target.

The hat sailed upward. Douglas sighted and fired, blasting the entire crown of the hat into bits.

The time had come for the chief to speak.

"Clatsop cannot shoot like you!" he declared firmly. "Wanapah cannot shoot like you!"

Many times after that, Douglas made use of what he had learned in Cockqua's camp. Whenever he approached a new Indian village, he waited until curious eyes were watching him. Then, pretending that he believed himself entirely alone, he would bring down a flying bird, doing it as if it were as simple as scratching a flea bite.

Weeks later, Cockqua visited Douglas. He brought along three English-style hats that the little Indian girl had made. And he proudly presented specimens of the *Vaccinium ovatum,* the box blueberry Douglas had said he wanted.

Through all of Douglas' wanderings that summer, the cones of the great pine still hung on their tall spires, far beyond his reach. In desperation, he had attempted to climb one of the younger giants, only to find that its tip would not bear his weight.

And there was still another species—a kingly pine—which was often in his thoughts. He had not seen it, but he'd heard that it grew on the southern reaches of the Willamette River, and he'd seen its seeds, which the Indians used raw as food. One day, he promised himself, he'd find it.

Meanwhile he was lured on one green pilgrimage after another. When he was too tired to walk, he crawled on his hands and knees. But there came a time, just when many of the seeds were ripening in the October warmth, when even his determination was not enough.

Chapter Six

Gift of Lightning

The *William and Ann*, after summer-long explorations and trading along the coast, was preparing to sail for England at last. Douglas worked feverishly at Fort Vancouver, sorting and packing the hundreds of specimens on hand. He planned to travel with them down river and personally supervise their being loaded onto the ship. But the day before he was to set out, he fell on a rusty nail and pierced one of his legs near the knee. The wound became inflamed and so painful that Douglas could scarcely stand.

Dr. McLoughlin said firmly that it was impossible for Douglas to attempt the ninety-mile journey to Fort George, and the pain in his leg forced Douglas to agree. The boxes of specimens would have to be put on board the vessel without his help.

A large abscess formed on the knee joint and for days

he fretted in his cedar hut, transcribing his notes into his journal, listing the plants he had found, and watching with envy as Billy made trips into the woods where precious seeds and fruits were ripening. He tortured himself with visions of the specimen boxes being stored in some damp corner of the ship where they would rot before arrival in England. And he mourned over not seeing Scouler and other ship members before their departure.

Finally, at the end of two weeks, his leg had healed enough for him to limp about. With his old knapsack on his shoulders, he set out on his trails. It was useless to think about the ship now. No doubt it was well on its way toward Cape Horn.

He was hobbling about near the fort when Tamto, his crooked face shaped in something resembling a smile, ran up to him. "White-headed Eagle get message from other lodge. Big shippo still in river. Bad winds keep it there."

Douglas' heart leaped. If he started at once, perhaps there was still a chance of seeing his shipmates and inspecting the cargo. "You—me—three other Indians get canoe—*kineve*—ready," he told Tamto. "We go toward sea, much quick. I give tobacco, nails, beads."

"*Queentschich*? How many?" Tamto demanded, settling down to haggle. He pointed at the metal buttons on Douglas' jacket. *"Queentschich cill-cill?"*

"Buttons?" Douglas held up three fingers. Tamto shook his head. Five fingers. Tamto still shook his head. Douglas held up eight fingers, all the buttons his coat possessed.

Tamto smiled crookedly and nodded.

A stubborn wind was blowing from the sea when Douglas set out with his three Indian companions and Billy. The canoe made only twenty miles the first day. On the next day, Sunday, time was lost in applying fresh pine gum to the canoe's seams. Skipping breakfast, the group set out, Douglas paddling with the rest. They had not gone more than a few miles when the current twisted the canoe off course so that they were headed toward a stump. The prow jarred against the fanged wood, and the canoe ripped from one end to the other. Water foamed through the gash.

Alarmed, Douglas and the others paddled toward shore. The water was churning around their knees by the time they reached a shallow where they could leap out and drag the injured craft on shore.

While the Indians repaired the canoe, Douglas acted as cook. A good meal now and there would be no need to stop again before night.

When it was mended, the canoe again took to the water. Douglas, his eyes on the western horizon, found the lingering pain in his still swollen leg almost matched by the growing ache in his shoulders and the stinging blisters on his palms. Darkness found him and his company across from the Indian village on Oak Point. They were hailed from shore and as they paused, an Indian canoe came swiftly across the water bringing news from Scouler that the ship would not be leaving for a few days. They decided to camp for the night and complete the journey the next day.

Morning brought an angry swell from the sea that strained paddling strength to the utmost. They had hoped to reach the river's mouth soon after dawn. When they finally headed across the broad harbor, a thin mist clinging to the water and shore, it was nine o'clock.

Douglas peered through the mist, seeking the ship. Perhaps a thicker patch of mist concealed it. Beaching the canoe beyond Fort George, he limped as fast as he could toward high ground. Billy raced ahead. Douglas was halfway to the top of the slope when an Indian and his squaw appeared. With a few grunting words and signs, the Indian gave Douglas the news. The "shippo" had sailed one hour ago.

Unbelieving, Douglas clambered to the top of the promontory and stared out to sea. There, almost within hailing distance, its sails whiter than the pelicans and gulls, was the *William and Ann*. Obviously, some last-minute decision had changed plans.

Slowly, Douglas limped back down toward the canoe. One hour. It might as well have been a week.

"*Cill-cill?*" Tamto spoke up at Douglas' shoulder.

For an instant, Douglas was tempted to toss him his whole coat. But he wrenched the buttons off one by one, and gave them to the Indian.

With a sigh, Douglas started off along the bay. Beyond was the village of Chief Concomly, smoke drifting from the roof openings of the lodges. The old chief, at least, was a friend to count on.

At twilight, when he arrived at the chief's camp, he found Concomly's brother Tha-a-muxi there on a visit from Gray's Harbor to the north. Unlike most of the Indians, who managed to pluck out their beards, Tha-a-muxi had a heavy, bristly black growth which gave him the name: The Beard. Like Concomly, he was an admirer of the English and had managed to add a few pieces of white man's finery to his wardrobe, including a long-dead watch that hung from his belt.

Tha-a-muxi invited Douglas to accompany him to Gray's Harbor for botanizing, and Concomly offered to ferry them across the mouth of the Columbia in his big war canoe with twelve of his tribesmen.

But now the weather struck full force. Together with his Indian friends, Douglas struggled to keep the supplies and food from being washed away. But the waves carried off one bit of cargo after another and nearly succeeded in carrying off the men as well. They reached land finally, drenched and shaken.

Douglas' knee was beginning to throb again. Trying to ignore it, he helped the Indians portage the heavy canoe over the rocks and brush, woods and gullies, for four tough miles across Cape Disappointment. On reaching Willapa Bay, the north indentation of the Cape, heavy fog and rain met them. For two days they were stormbound. Sleet joined the rain. They had practically no food, and no dry wood for fire. Hunting for roots and kinnikinnick berries to eat, Douglas felt nearly as much a part of the wilderness as any of the Indians.

As the canoe plowed northward again toward the next cape thrusting between it and Gray's Harbor, even Billy's high spirits failed. He lay glumly at Douglas' feet, his wet coat the color of the fog.

Across the bay, another portage faced them. Sixteen miles this time. Douglas ordered two of the Indians to take the canoe back to Concomly, while he and Tha-a-muxi and the remaining braves went on foot.

Even without the burden of the canoe, Douglas found himself stumbling toward the end of the fourteen-hour-

long hike. For two days he had eaten scarcely anything.
But the chance of finding new plant species had driven
him. The summer was nearly over and his instructions
from the Society requested that he spend no more than
a year in this land.

As they neared the south shore of Gray's Harbor, the
black-bearded Tha-a-muxi moderated his own stride to
walk at Douglas' side.

Still no sun relieved the banks of fog, and the wind
drove with stinging force. Shivering, the group dragged
some pine branches and old cedar-bark mats together to
try to make a shelter as they camped for the night. Side
by side, Tha-a-muxi and Douglas huddled under their
flimsy covering. When Tha-a-muxi found a precious bit
of tobacco in his pouch and tamped it in his pipe for a
smoke of comradeship, Douglas was unable to take
more than a weak puff before he coughed and spat the
smoke out.

Tha-a-muxi looked at him sadly. "Oh," he cried, eyeing the smoke, "why do you throw away the food? See,
I take it in my belly." He drew in a great lungful of
smoke, swallowing it.

In spite of his misery, Douglas smiled at the old Indian. Tha-a-muxi's greed for swallowing every bit of

smoke resulted in his often falling down in a fit of stupe-
faction.

The storm howled on through the night and through
the following day. Douglas, exhausted and weak from
hunger, could not stir an inch from his sodden shelter.
Toward dusk, the wind let up a bit. Dragging his gun
along beside him, he crawled out a few rods away from
the camp site, desperately seeking some kind of game.
Sitting in a row on the shore of a nearby stream was a
flock of ducks.

Douglas raised his gun and fired. Five of the birds
fell with one shot.

As the Indians retrieved the birds, Douglas answered
Tha-a-muxi's awed and questioning look by saying: "It
was not my magic but the magic of the Great Chief
above." He pointed heavenward.

Tha-a-muxi nodded solemnly. "*Hias tye-yea.* Is he
greater chief than the chiefs of King George?"

"Aye!" Douglas declared.

The ducks were cooked quickly. One hungry Indian
ate most of his raw. Another burned the feathers off
rather than pluck them, to save time. Douglas lost his
appetite suddenly, and ate very little.

The group decided to walk on toward the Chehalis
River where it flowed into Gray's Harbor for it was there

that Tha-a-muxi's tribe lived. They were just starting out when a canoe appeared on the bay. The Chehalis had seen the campfire and had sent a canoe to transport them across the bay to the river.

Gratefully, Douglas and Billy took their places in the canoe with the rest.

At the camp, Douglas rested for several days as the guest of Tha-a-muxi. He was the first white man ever to be the guest of the Chehalis, and as he sat resting in the chief's own lodge he found that he was not bothered much by the squalor and stench, although it was the worst he had encountered. He was too grateful to be critical and when he recorded the experience in his journal he wrote only that he had received "every kindness and all the hospitality Indian courtesy could suggest."

As soon as he was able to move about freely again, he began botanizing, still driven by the need to make every minute count. Seeds of wild licorice and beargrass found their way into his vasculum. With Tha-a-muxi, he talked over a plan to make his way to the source of the Chehalis River, and the chief said he would go with him.

They set out together in a canoe. More rain, plus dangerous cascades, made Douglas abandon his plan after sixty miles. He then decided to turn southward, following the Cowlitz River toward the Columbia before going eastward toward his home base.

Tha-a-muxi said that he must return to his own people. Standing before Douglas, the chief put his hand to his heavy beard and asked, "I entreat you, Man of Grass, to shave me so that I may more resemble one of King George's chiefs."

Douglas got out his razor and in a short while a clean-shaven Tha-a-muxi stood beaming at him.

After thanking Douglas for the service, the chief added, "It would make my heart warm, for you to let King George's chiefs across the great water know of me when you speak to them with paper."

Douglas said he would be glad to do this and in order to let Tha-a-muxi see that he meant it, he wrote a few appropriate words as the Indian watched. When he showed it to Tha-a-muxi, the chief put his hand across his eyes and studied the writing through his fingers as if he were looking at the dead.

With real regret, Douglas parted from the chief and made his way slowly homeward. He reached Fort Vancouver in mid-November, after an absence of twenty-five days. It had been the most miserable trip he had ever made, and the most fruitless.

With the rain falling almost daily and his knee inflamed again, his hopes of collecting much more were
small. During the long days ahead he could do little but
copy his notes, put his specimens in order, and try to
keep his thoughts cheerful.

Then, on the eighteenth of November, came a cry
that sent his spirits up. The annual Hudson's Bay Company's express had been sighted at a distance on the
river. At last, at last, there would be mail!

As soon as the boats announced their approach by
the firing of guns, Douglas hobbled down to the landing
with all the others. There should be letters from Hooker,
Sabine, his brother John, and all the rest. It was a long
time since he had heard from home.

"Nay, Billy," he said, bending down to his shaggy
partner, "there'll be no mail for you. But I'll share
mine."

The two boats, twenty men in each, approached the
landing. The voyageurs were dressed in bright shirts and
wore scarfs about their throats, for the occasion. On
shore, one of the Company employees played a loud
welcome on his bagpipes.

Douglas waited impatiently for the clerk to go through
the pouch containing the mail. The pile of letters grew
smaller as the clerk handed them around. Finally there

were only a half-dozen left. Then five. Four. The last letter appeared in the clerk's hand—and was handed to Dr. McLoughlin.

"Is there—nothing for me?" Douglas asked.

The clerk shook his head.

"But I don't understand! Hooker—Sabine—Mr. Murray—"

"Didn't you hear?" the clerk asked. "The express left Hudson's Bay a week before the ship from England arrived."

Slowly Douglas walked away, Billy tagging behind. One week. One hour. Time! Always the treachery of time.

That night, listening to the steady rain beat on his bark hut, Douglas felt that he had been deserted by his friends at home. In his heart he knew that this was not true, but it was bitter to realize that the letters that must have come for him were even now lying thousands of miles away across the continent.

Sometime in the night a great bell of thunder pealed, waking him. There was a crash as of lightning striking some forest giant and splitting its heart. Billy sat up on his haunches, nose pointed at the roof, and howled.

At dawn, Douglas was awakened by a swift, sly movement near the hut's entrance. He glimpsed the black hair and twisted, scarred face before the Indian reached into the tent, then started away.

In spite of his bad knee, Douglas went after him. Taking his visitor by surprise, he reached out, grabbed a handful of black hair and spun the man around.

"No wake white chief," the wriggling Tamto explained. "Many *cill-cill*."

Cill-cill! His temper as inflamed as his knee, Douglas exclaimed, "You've been paid, you thieving rascal. Go away. Get out. If I find you sneaking—"

Tamto wriggled free and dived toward the hut. He stooped, then straightened, palms out. In each hand lay a wet, gleaming pine cone. "See! Much storm knock-knock in night. Me watch—run. Find *cill-cill* from big chief of trees."

Douglas stared. Unconsciously, he clapped his hand to his mouth like any Chinook registering astonishment —but not dread. No, there was no doubt about it. Tamto—the blessed wretch—had brought him shining, beautiful, ripe-to-bursting cones from the monarch of the forests. His *Pinus taxifolia*! He turned to Tamto, only the thought of the man's prolific fleas preventing him from embracing him.

"We smoke together, Tamto! Come in. I give you much beads, thread, tobacco, for the *cill-cill*. You great friend of Grass Man." He took the cones in his hands, holding them as if they were rare jewels.

It was New Year's Day, 1826. Douglas sat in his new quarters in Dr. McLoughlin's half-finished dwelling, his journal open before him. The rain dripped steadily on the roof boards. On Christmas Eve it had poured into his cedar-bark hut until the floor was covered with water. Now he was dry, at least, but that was almost the only comfort.

Although his knee was much improved, it had prevented him from horseback riding on Christmas Day with the rest of the company. Now only his own melancholy kept him from the celebrations of the new year.

Thoughtfully, he wrote in his journal: "Commencing a year in such a far removed corner of the earth, where I am nearly destitute of civilized society, there is some scope for reflection." Last year at the same time he had been sailing expectantly between the island of Juan Fernandez and the Galapagos, on the way to his first great adventure. He wrote on: "I am nowhere, and God only knows where I may be next. In all probability, if a change does not take place, I will shortly be consigned to the tomb."

They were dreary thoughts for a man who was still not twenty-seven. But as he closed the journal, he felt a shudder—and a return of the old, hot impatience. There was so much to do.

How, when he was under orders to return to England in this new year of 1826? Although he had collected much, there was still much that he had not. There were the Columbia's tributaries gleaming toward the Rocky Mountains, their riches still scarcely touched. There were the Blue Mountains—and the white cone of Mount Hood that he might some day try to climb.

He leaned back in his chair, an old light coming into his eyes. "I can't go back now, orders or no," he said aloud. "I can't leave before the job is finished!" He picked Billy up in his arms and stood facing the window. "If the Society does not like it—well, there is nothing they can do." A touch of humor lighted his features. "The mail service being what it is, laddie, they can't get a letter back to me in time to prevent my staying. And by then there'll be a ton of seeds in my pack." He put Billy down and sat at the table again. "I'll write to Sabine now. I'll tell him that I'll labor most cheerfully without any pay if they'll just give me enough for a little clothing. Isn't that right, Billy?"

Billy recognized the familiar determination in his master's voice. There was nothing for a faithful companion to do but give a hearty bark of agreement.

Chapter Seven

High Water

On his way up the Columbia River in March, on an extended trip to the interior, a new difficulty began to bother Douglas seriously. His eyesight had been poor for a long time, but now a kind of mist swam across his vision, even with his spectacles on. The dimness was occurring more often, at times coming between him and his target when he was shooting for game or for tree specimens.

Traveling with two heavily-laden boats of the yearly express from Vancouver to Hudson's Bay, he tried to keep his eyes closed against the hard glare of the sun. But there was too much to see and watch for. In order to justify his staying here, he must work even harder than before.

He heard the grunting of the young pigs crowded into the second boat, the plaintive call of one of the three

103

calves. The livestock was destined for the new outpost, Fort Colville, up at Kettle Falls. His own special cargo, a hundred pounds of paper, given to him by Dr. McLoughlin, was destined for drying and wrapping green treasure from The Dalles, the Spokane River, the Walla Walla, Priest's Rapids, the Okanagan, and, he hoped, the Blue Mountains. He had reduced his wardrobe to two shirts, two handkerchiefs, a blanket and coat, one pair of shoes, but no stockings, to make room for the paper. Soon, he thought with grim humor, he would be wearing only an otter-skin robe or breechcloth like the savages.

The commander of the express, John McLeod, pointed to the great rocks that cluttered the river beyond. "We may have trouble from the Indians when we camp for our portage around Celilo Falls. Bad spot here—especially with our tempting cargo of livestock.

A short while later, camping among the rocks of The Dalles, Douglas realized that McLeod was right. Indians had collected from everywhere, it seemed. Almost five hundred of them were milling around, trying to sneak near the boats, muttering resentfully that they had been short-changed in the trading for salmon. A guard was posted all night long and though the Indians restrained themselves to threats, their ugly temper intensified.

During the portage over Celilo Falls, Douglas kept himself tensed for the expected attack. At the falls, as the sweating boatmen relaxed momentarily, the boats resting at the water's edge, several Indians stole around behind the men's backs. Before anyone realized what the Indians were up to, they had begun throwing water on the locks of the guns stored in one boat.

McLeod leaped to his feet. "Get the boats into the water!" he ordered the crew.

The voyageurs started toward their vessels but a band of Indians leaped in between.

McLeod rushed forward, commanding the foremost native to stand back. The Indian bared his teeth in defiance. McLeod, his face red with anger, gave the Indian a shove that sent him sprawling.

Douglas seized his gun and loaded it with buckshot. There, just beyond McLeod, another Indian stood drawing his bow, the arrow directed at McLeod's back.

"*Keya!* No!" Douglas yelled, bringing his gun up and pointing it at the archer. "Drop that bow—or I shoot!"

McLeod whirled around to see the archer on one side, Douglas on the other.

The Indian stayed as he was, his arrow still glinting against the bow, defiance in his eyes.

"If you let that arrow fly," Douglas said, almost whispering, "you're a dead man." Though his voice was under control, he felt his bad knee tremble. Everyone else had turned, staring silently. Douglas heard a fly buzz past his ear and, far away, a horse neighed. A thread of perspiration dripped down his neck.

A tall Indian with strong, handsome features and wide shoulders moved forward, the bracelets on his arms glinting. Douglas felt a surge of admiration. This Indian, six-and-a-half feet tall, was the finest figure of a man he had ever seen. The Indian moved to the archer's side, spoke one short sentence, and the archer lowered his bow.

The deadlock was over. Slowly, Douglas lowered his gun. At his side, a voyageur whispered, "A horse Indian. A Cayuse chief."

McLeod clasped Douglas' hand, then the chief's. In a moment, McLeod and the Cayuse were smoking together while the other Indians slunk back to a respectful distance.

Looking closely at the chief, Douglas saw that nothing but a bare piece of brass wire hung from the perforated septum of the Indian's nose. Ordinarily, some bead or stone hung from the wire as a decoration.

Douglas questioned the Indian about this. The Cayuse

explained that his favorite ornament, a glittering button that had once belonged to a white chief, had been lost.

Douglas fumbled in his pocket. "You wait. I will give you something even better. A white man's *higua*—money." Borrowing an awl from one of the boatmen, he bored a hole in the one shilling he had brought from England and gave it to the chief who hung it proudly from the ring in his nose.

The Indian radiated gratitude. Solemnly he declared that the whites would not be bothered again. Now, eternal friendship should exist between them.

Peace for the price of a shilling was a good Scottish bargain, Douglas reflected that night as he and Billy lay under the stars. But not so good a bargain that he did not keep one eye open, watchfully, for most of the night.

The express traveled onward, northeast, through barren, sagebrush-stippled country toward the Spokane River over five hundred miles distant. Douglas walked as much as he rode in the boat, he and Billy making their way along shore while the crew paddled upstream. Where the water was too turbulent, the boatmen had to get out themselves, and haul the boats along at the end of ropes. Parsley, mustard, wild currants, flowers, and sagebrush found their way into Douglas' knapsack. Occasionally he saw deer, wolves, foxes, and badgers in the brushwood. His knee still bothered him and the sun glancing off the sandy hills made his eyes ache.

On April 11, the express reached the Spokane River. There the Company's commandant in the interior, John Dease, invited Douglas to be his guest for a time. Douglas said goodbye to the crew who were going on northward before they would swing east and travel across the wilderness to Hudson's Bay. It was there that the Company had its headquarters, the focal point of the fur trade.

Along with the wealth of furs would go a wealth of seeds. Nervously, Douglas watched the boats depart, carrying with them his great harvest. Watching the water-wheels left by the dipping paddles, he seemed to see a shining froth of flowers. For if the seeds arrived safely in England, they would eventually clothe it and Europe with the colors that had shimmered on the banks of the Columbia.

Giving McLeod a farewell wave, he turned away, his mind already busy with the tasks ahead.

The next weeks were as busy as the preceding had been. Douglas, with his host John Dease, followed the express to Kettle Falls and gathered more riches in his knapsack. The scenery impressed him as the most magnificent he had seen—high, rugged mountains, fertile valleys, the falls pounding down twenty-five feet in a white wall. Showers of rain plagued his botanizing en route, however, together with snow on the hills. In spite of that, his pack grew fat with more specimens.

On a trip from Fort Colville at Kettle Falls to Spokane House to get his gun fixed by Jocko Finlay, the only gunsmith available, Douglas was forced to swim across the Methow River on his back while he held his supplies up out of the water. Billy and the horses swam more comfortably, on their bellies.

On his return to the fort, Douglas had to swim the river again. This time, he suffered severe chills from the cold water. Having no medicine, he tried to sweat off the chill by strenuous exercise. But he could not shake the pain that had settled between his shoulder blades. When he finally reached Fort Colville, feverish and worn out, he had to take to bed.

Out of bed again, he completed his cure by walking twenty miles up the Columbia and back on one day, and the same distance southward the next! For good measure, he hiked for ten miles up the Kettle River, the first European, to his knowledge, ever to invade the banks of that stream.

With three big bundles of plants and over forty kinds of seeds, he traveled southward back toward Fort Walla

Walla for an expedition to the Blue Mountains. Trader
Samuel Black of that fort negotiated for a guide for
Douglas while the botanist continued his search for
plants. Here there were no cool forests of mighty pines
to shelter him. Sweltering heat and burning sand, with
high winds which hurled the sand into his blinking eyes,
made his eyelids become inflamed. He could scarcely see
an object ten yards away. Many of the Indians, too, he
noticed, had sore, red-rimmed eyes like his. Also, the
sand of the river got mixed into their stores of dried
salmon and almost every Indian's teeth were worn down
from chewing on the grit.

After much smoking from a large stone pipe, and
hours of bargaining carried on by Black and a Canadian
interpreter with a Cayuse Indian, the deal for a guide
was settled. The dialect spoken by this Cayuse, however,
was one Douglas could not understand so Black recommended that the twelve-year-old son of the Canadian,
Young Wasp, go along on the expedition as interpreter.
The route was laid out and supplies and horses arranged
for. Satisfied, Douglas went to bed in a rough cave he
had chosen for the night.

Sometime toward dawn he was awakened by a sound
as of something being dragged along the floor near his
pillow. He sat up cautiously, peering through the pale
light, expecting to see an Indian pillaging his stores.

What he saw was a horde of woodrats. Billy, starting up from under the blanket he shared with Douglas, growled but stayed where he was.

Douglas stared in astonishment at the huge rats. Directly across from him, one big rat was carrying away his inkstand!

Douglas drew his gun out from under the blanket, raised it, and gave the inkstand thief the full charge of shot. The inkstand clattered against a rock and the rat gave a death leap. The other rats scattered.

A quick inspection revealed that the rats had devoured every seed he had collected, had eaten through a bundle of dried plants, and had carried off his shaving brush and razor. When Douglas had got over his dismay, he turned to the rat he had killed, determined to salvage the creature as a zoological specimen, at least. However, the rat was too riddled to make a good specimen. Measuring it, Douglas found that it was a foot and a half long from its black-whiskered nose to the tip of its hairy tail.

This was Douglas' first experience with the creature called a "pack rat" because of its fondness for carrying off a variety of objects to its nest.

In spite of the long negotiations and careful preparations, Douglas' trip to the Blue Mountains turned out to be another grueling journey filled with unforeseen difficulties. The first trouble arose on the fourth day of the trip. About fifteen hundred feet from the summit of the range, the horses could go no farther because of the deep snow. The Cayuse guide began to balk, saying that he was afraid to climb higher. "Bad spirits in mountains," he said, according to Young Wasp's interpretation.

"Tell him," Douglas ordered Young Wasp, "that I want to cross over and descend to the Grand Ronde."

Young Wasp transmitted the order to the guide—or so Douglas believed. The guide continued to shake his head and gesture in fright.

There was only one thing to do: go on alone. With Billy, his gun, and some paper, Douglas set out. Lacking snowshoes, his feet sank through the white surface with every step. And his blue glasses were unequal to the rays of the sun, even though heavy clouds covered it for minutes at a time. With eyes half-closed against the glare, he labored onward until, toward the summit, he found the snow crusted enough to bear his weight.

At last, over six thousand feet above sea level, he paused to rest briefly before his descent to the valley beyond. Here, with the peaks and furrows, rocks and snow fields spread out before him, he took deep, triumphant breaths of the cold air. Clouds completely covered the sun and he removed his blue glasses, searching these heights above timberline for interesting alpine species.

"Think of it, Billy," he said to the terrier, "this is the first time a Scottish terrier has ever been here." No European person had been on the heights before, either, and perhaps no American. And judging by the trembling guide, Indians feared the place.

Wind whipped at his plaid jacket and he frowned, noticing its sudden fierceness. He had better get on before the weather grew worse.

He had scarcely started walking again when a great billow of thunder broke over the peaks, accompanied by rain. He glanced around for an overhanging rock under which he could take shelter, but there was nothing. The rain thickened, pelting his face. Hail began pouring around him, nicking his cheeks, battering at his eyelids. Billy turned and trotted back toward camp, then stopped, waiting for Douglas to follow. With every crash of thunder, the dog's courage wilted a little more.

With rain and hail streaming against him and his jacket dripping moisture, Douglas hesitated, hoping the storm would leave as quickly as it had come. A closer study of the cloud-curdled sky blasted his hope. Brushing the cold rain from his eyes, he turned and followed

Billy. Getting pneumonia wasn't going to serve the cause of botany.

When he reached the camp where Young Wasp and the guide sullenly waited, he was drenched through. After a useless attempt to build a fire in the wind, he gave up, stripped off the wettest of his clothes, rolled himself in his damp blanket and tried to sleep.

The cold gnawed through the blanket and into his skin. Finally, at midnight, the winds let up and he decided to try once more to make a fire. When he unrolled the blanket and attempted to stand up, his knees were so numb that they would not support him. Crawling to his stack of supplies, he found a rough towel, then sat scrubbing at his knees until he had restored their circulation enough for him to stand up and get a fire going. After making a cup of hot tea, he hung up his clothes to dry. Back in his blanket, he managed to sleep until early dawn.

With the new day, his spirits revived and he suggested to his companions that they try to cross over the summit at a lower elevation. Again the guide had objections. They would have trouble crossing the Umatilla River, he said. On top of that, his people and the Snake tribe were at war in the area and the Snakes would steal their horses and probably kill Douglas, Young Wasp,

and himself. The guide's trembling attitude suggested
that the real reasons for his reluctance were deeper.
Douglas, noticing a crafty and mischievous look in
Young Wasp's eyes, wondered if that boy might not be
responsible.

Well, he could not undertake the journey alone.
Resigned, he settled down to botanizing for two days
where he was. He was rewarded by discovering a certain
peony, *Paeonia brownii*, the first ever found in America. Another find was a golden lupine which he named
after Sabine.

He and his companions returned to the post at Walla
Walla. There Douglas tried to arrange for another expedition to the mountains. This time the Cayuse refused
even to start and, at the first opportunity, he fled entirely.

Later Douglas learned that Young Wasp had filled
the guide with alarming tales of the Grass Man's "big
medicine"—saying that he was in league with the evil
spirits and could kill him, or turn him into a grizzly bear
to run and live in the mountains without ever seeing his
family again.

With a new guide, Douglas went back to the Blue
Mountains. Again he made his way along the snowline,
hunting plants for two days. He found nothing except

the painful glare of sunlight, and fatigue. His eyes now troubled him so that it was only in the mornings that he could read or write. Disheartened, he returned to Walla Walla. There he had a chance to send his collections of the past month to Fort Vancouver with a trader. Along with ninety-seven species of plants, and almost fifty packages of seeds, he sent a less gunshot-riddled specimen of one of the rats that had stolen many of his seeds. Douglas went part of the way down the river with the trader.

At The Dalles the party met a fur brigade returning from Hudson's Bay. The brigade carried letters and this time a number of the letters were addressed to David Douglas, Esq. Letters from Hooker, Sabine, his own family.

Douglas opened the letters eagerly. His own letter announcing his decision to stay at the Columbia for another year had not reached England in time for there to be any answer in these letters, but he did find out that his first big collection of plants had arrived there. Of the collection, Sabine wrote: "All you have done has given perfect satisfaction and my only wish about you is to see you safe again in England."

Douglas shook his head wonderingly. Sabine obviously thought that the first shipment of specimens was all that was to be expected, and yet he was perfectly sat-

isfied! What would he be when more shipments of boxes
and cases and wrappers arrived?

During the night, Douglas got up four times to read
and reread his letters until he could almost recite them
by heart to the dozing and disinterested Billy.

News from home was like a battery supplying him
with fresh energy. He set out for the 110-mile journey
back to Walla Walla, walking every step of the way. Two
days after he had been at Walla Walla he set out again,
this time with a party of men going up the Snake River
to purchase horses from the Indians. Hundred-degree
heat beat down on the group. There was little to eat but
horsemeat. At the junction of the Snake and Clearwater
rivers, the men began their bargaining with the five hundred Nez Percé, Palouse, and Chamuiemuch Indians
camped there.

While the trading was going on, Douglas went on
horseback toward mountains to the southeast for several
days of plant-hunting. He returned to camp to find the
Indians and the traders at the point of war. After many
speeches, during some of which the Indian orators wept
and cried aloud in their impassioned speeches, the affair
was settled and ended in the usual way: an exchange of
gifts.

Traveling on with the party, which now included 114

horses, Douglas arrived at Fort Colville. A message from McLoughlin had arrived saying that a ship, the *Dryad*, was at the Columbia and planned to leave for England in early September.

Douglas went to Chief Trader Dease to ask about getting a boat down the Columbia to Fort Vancouver. If he could reach there before the ship left he could send off his collections. It was now late August.

"The river is at its worst," Dease said. "Floodwater and all the melting snow. You can't make it in a small canoe."

"Well, can I get a big canoe?"

Dease shook his head. "There's nothing going that way now."

"But I must go!" Douglas insisted. "Even if I have to walk."

"Six hundred miles is a long walk," Dease said. "Perhaps I can arrange for a horse to do the walking, under you."

On August 19, Douglas found himself with not one horse, but three, and well supplied with pemmican, sugar and tea, plus a pair of deerskin trousers which Dease had given him. For his guide he had a Spokane Indian, one to whom he could communicate only in sign language.

They followed the shore of the river southward and

then east for three days, enduring the painfully familiar hardships—the same blood-greedy mosquitoes, burning heat and alkali-bitter water which neither Douglas nor the horses could drink.

Racing against time, as he had a year ago when the *William and Ann* was due to leave, Douglas procured a canoe and two Indian boatmen at Fort Okanagan and set out downstream, defying the Columbia to do its worst. He acted as steersman, standing in the stern and wielding the long paddle against the treacherous currents. Like a petty thief, the river contented itself with carrying off the one cooking utensil he had left, and drenched his precious tea and sugar. Weak from exhaustion, he arrived at Fort Walla Walla on August 25.

Scarcely taking time to do more than get a bigger canoe and two fresh guides, he went on again the next day—and all of the following night in order to steal past a certain camp of Indians who were known for their light-fingered talents.

At The Dalles, where the river boiled among the giant rocks, the Columbia made a more bold attack, and hurtled the canoe against the rocks. Although Douglas managed to scramble from the wreckage, all of the insect specimens he had obtained, plus many seeds, and a pistol, went plunging into the water.

With the help of the Indians he got a small canoe

and more guides. When they reached the Cascades, the water pouring over the rapids was so fierce, and the wind so strong, that Douglas had to pack all of his supplies on his back, lugging them over the high rocks while the Indians struggled with the canoe.

On the next to the last day of August he arrived at Fort Vancouver. As he walked up the low plain from the landing place, the men at the fort stared as if at a ghost—a ghost in a ragged straw hat, torn leather trousers, shoeless and stockingless, his face weather-burned and lined with fatigue, his hair as tangled as his dog's.

"We thought we'd never see you again," Dr. McLoughlin admitted as he shook Douglas' hand. "The river's higher than anyone remembers its being before." He leaned on his gold-headed cane, inspecting Douglas. "You look as if you've had a swim or two."

"I did get damp a few times," Douglas admitted.

"Come along now. Some dry clothes and a good rest—"

"Aye! I need them. But I'll have to rest later, sir. The ship for England—"

"It's still there," McLoughlin told him. "And will be until day after tomorrow. I'm sending a boat of cargo to her tomorrow."

Tomorrow! Douglas groaned. That left him scarcely

a day to pack all of his own cargo of over a hundred
seeds, chests of dried plants, birds, bones, twigs, animal
skins. . . . And there were letters to write. "Excuse
me, sir! I'll have to get at it. Billy, come along!"

Forcing his weary legs into motion, Douglas hurried
toward his quarters in McLoughlin's house.

The first thing he saw when he entered the room was
the huge, seventeen-inch-long pine cone he had left sitting on his rough writing table. He paused, picked it
up, and studied it again. It was a cone from the mysterious pine on the Willamette River, one that a fur hunter,
Baptiste McKay, had brought to him in February. So
great a cone could come only from a great tree. Rest or
no rest, he must go and see the tree for himself and ob-
tain its twigs and gum and seeds before another winter
fastened him indoors. For, once the winter was over, he
would have to return at last to England.

Chapter Eight

The Shining Cones

It was late September. On the lower reaches of the Willamette River, rain dripped from the foliage and glittered in the thick fur of grizzlies which prowled near the rough trail following the river's west bank. Marching in single file, a party of thirty white men, their horses, and several Indians, headed southward on their annual search for furs. In the lead walked two men, tugging at the reins of their horses. One was the expedition's commander, Alexander McLeod; the other was Douglas. Both carried guns held ready for game but Douglas stopped often to study the vegetation, which was to him more exciting. At his heels still trotted Billy, the terrier, looking as tired as his master.

The party's progress was painfully slow. Time after

122

time the men halted to hack at trees fallen across the path, or at jungle vines that threatened to trip the horses. At other places, deep streams barred the way. Horses straying from their overnight camps had to be rounded up. Deer or wild fowl had to be hunted for food. Rainy weather turned parts of the trail into a black mire, while steep and stony hills injured the horses' feet.

As the party approached a burned-over clearing, Douglas commented, "I'll not find any specimens in that charred brushwood."

"You may find a few more blisters on your feet by night," his companion answered. "They say the Indians in these parts burn these areas deliberately so that the deer are crowded into the unburnt areas. That way they can hunt them more easily. We'll head for that green area yonder and maybe we can pick off a fat buck for our own stomachs."

Douglas looked at the burned-over land mournfully. It seemed he could smell the burnt perfume of tiny blossoms that had been destroyed. Black ash drifted up from his feet to plug his nostrils and darken his face. As for blisters, his boots seemed so much paper against the thrust of tough grass and brambles.

A tangle of scorched blackberry bushes obstructed the trail. Faces and arms were scratched badly, and hairs from Billy's gray coat were left waving from the thorny boughs.

One of the hunters shot a deer and that night the party dined on venison, the first meat that they had had for several days.

The next morning, two hours before dawn, another hunter, John Kennedy, decided to scout the territory for more venison to add to their reserves. Douglas, too, was out before dawn. Around ten he returned to camp to deposit the morning's botanical collection. Except for one of the men who had a sprained ankle, the camp was deserted.

Douglas was putting flower specimens in an improvised press when he heard a high-pitched yell. His horse, tethered nearby, reared and whinnied. Douglas moved to the horse's side, stroking its muzzle. Billy, too, gave a good imitation of a whinny as he sniffed the air.

A man, George Howell, rushed into the clearing. "Grizzly!" he yelled. "After Kennedy. Come on! I ran out of shot." He seized a pouch and started off, loading his gun as he ran.

Douglas raced after him. When Howell stopped suddenly, Douglas almost crashed into him. "Look!" said Howell. Only ten feet ahead a young male grizzly stood, shoulders humped above the lowered head. The bear's upper lip drew back, exposing its wet, white teeth. Douglas struggled to get his gun into position just as the monster reared up, the long, heavy claws on its fore-feet stabbing the air. Douglas aimed, a memory of Tam-to's scarred face lurching through his mind. At that instant the hoarse cry for help came again.

Howell had his gun up. The bear lunged and met Howell's fire fullface. For a moment the bear stood grabbing at the air with his claws. A geyser of blood shot out between its eyes with such force that red drops sprayed against Douglas' shirt. Then the grizzly dropped, gave a small moan, and lay still.

Stumbling over the dead bear, Howell ran ahead, calling over his shoulder: "The one after Kennedy was bigger. Must be still after him, judging by that second yell!"

"There!" Douglas exclaimed, pointing to a small oak.

Kennedy, his clothes in ruins, was wedged into the tree's crotch, his face white. But there was no sign of another grizzly, though great tracks in the moist earth around the tree showed where the animal had been.

As Douglas and Howell helped Kennedy down, other members of the party appeared. Kennedy told through chattering teeth how he had been hunting and had come within ten yards of a giant grizzly before he knew of the beast's presence. He had made a bad shot that had infuriated the grizzly to attack.

"Fortunately," he said, "my clothes were so rotted with rain and sun, he ripped them off with one swipe—and sniffed them long enough for me to have time to climb this tree."

Studying the grizzly that Howell had killed, Kennedy shook his head. "Not the same one. The other was eight feet long if he was an inch. He ran off just before you came."

The men hunted some time for the giant grizzly but had no luck.

Several days later, however, as the band left the Willamette River valley, Baptiste McKay shot a female grizzly. Douglas traded an old blanket and some tobacco for the hide to use as a robe under him when sleeping on the cold, wet ground. Then, as the terrain grew even more difficult, his horse stumbling twice and skidding down stump-infested hills, Douglas removed his large vasculum from the mount's back. Wrapping the bearskin around his precious parcel, he strapped the load to his own shoulders.

"This grizzly will keep my back dry, at any rate," he commented.

He found more plants, together with other natural

history specimens, to add to his bearskin vasculum as the party entered new territory. Princely chestnuts added their seeds to his bag. At Elk Creek he found a beautiful evergreen, the California laurel. Quail and a great black California condor were taken and preserved and added to his pack.

By mid-October the band reached the Umpqua River. To the south lay a wilderness little known. A group of Umpqua Indians came to the camp and Douglas discovered that two of them understood Chinook. He asked the two if they knew of a mighty pine growing anywhere in the area.

They nodded vigorously but when it came to describing the exact location they grew vague and silent. Still, Douglas was reassured by their knowing about the pine and he made his plans to continue his search with one of the Indians from the fur party.

With Billy making a third, Douglas and a young Indian set off to the southeast. After traveling nine miles, they found it necessary to cross the river. Douglas turned carpenter and started building a raft. An hour's work made his hands so raw he could not use a hatchet any more. Also, the raft looked unpromisingly small.

In the morning, he found his hands still too sore for

work. He told the Indian to go back to the main camp and ask for help.

As soon as the Indian had gone, Douglas set out to hunt some meat. In several places he saw grizzly tracks and chuckled as Billy stepped carefully around them as if they were traps especially set for a Scottish terrier. The tracks that really interested Douglas at the moment were those of a deer, large tracks suggesting they belonged to a good-sized buck.

He had gone only a mile when he saw the animal. He aimed. The dimness that bothered him at times obscured his vision even as he fired so that his ball struck the buck in the shoulder. It was enough to lame the creature but not to kill it.

Dismayed, Douglas pursued the buck as it limped swiftly into the underbrush. The trail was easy enough to follow because of the flecks of blood left on the foliage, but it was rough with stones and snags. Just as he was coming within shooting distance of the buck, Douglas spied a pale, cream-colored bloom a few feet away. He went off the trail toward it.

Billy stopped suddenly, giving a sharp bark.

A piece of deadwood cracked under Douglas' weight. The next instant the earth went out from under him. As he fell he heard Billy bark again. The barking turned to a strange, humming roar and he thought vaguely:

What's wrong with Billy? Then all sound stopped and he lay still, one hand locked around a crooked piece of deadwood at the bottom of the deep gully.

Hours later, Douglas stirred and opened his eyes. He shook his head, overwhelmed by a feeling of nightmare. A shudder went through him and he stared, uncomprehendingly, at the dusky face of the Indian squatting beside him—the high cheekbones, the tattooed face, the matted black hair. Other tattooed Indians were behind the first one. Douglas struggled up on one elbow with a cry, but a pain tearing through his chest brought reality back. Now he remembered. The wounded deer. Billy's warning bark. The fall through nothingness. . . .

The Indians indicated with gestures that they were there to help him from the gully. Billy's barking must have called attention to him. Gratefully, Douglas put his arms over the shoulders of two sturdy-looking natives. They helped him to the top of the gully, and from there back to his camp. It would be impossible for him to continue his journey. With gestures, he asked the Indians to saddle his horse and load his supplies.

Seeing that the natives looked lean, Douglas offered all the venison he had brought with him, trying to convey his gratitude by more sign language.

He whittled off a stout branch from a tree. With that

and his gun as canes, he hobbled toward the horse, wondering how he could lead the animal and still support himself.

One of the Indians came forward and took the horse's reins.

Douglas felt a happy amazement. These Indians who had rarely if ever seen a white man before were among the friendliest he had met.

Limping along, he murmured to Billy, "We all but finished it up that time." He remembered what a Glasgow gardener had said to him years ago. *Ye must watch your headlongness, man. Some day ye may rush into that from which you canna get out again.* As if speaking to a witness, Douglas murmured: "Aye, but a man can't search for posies and pines and always keep his eyes on his feet!" No. The goal was the thing, not the bumbles on the path. And what was a cracked rib, after all, compared to the gardens he had carried on his back? Beautiful paths those seeds would make! Flowers for a world to wade through.

"Come along, lad," he said. "Let others be timid. We've no time for that."

Halfway to the camp, he met John Kennedy. Kennedy stared at the hobbling Man of Grass. "What happened?" he asked.

"I was attacked by an angry gully," Douglas said dryly as Kennedy helped him up onto the horse for the ride back to camp.

Traveling on down the Umpqua with Alexander Mc-Leod's party, Douglas still searched the hills and the horizon for the great pine, in vain. As they drew closer to the sea, the ocean hazed the atmosphere and the river began to show the influence of the tides. Some twenty miles from the sea, Centrenose, the principal chief of the area, visited the camp. With him were several of his squaws, their lower jaws tattooed from mouth to ear. The Indians brought salmon and Douglas was surprised to find that they seemed to know nothing of fishing with a net like the Chinooks on the Columbia. They killed their salmon with spears.

Douglas decided that he should retrace his steps along the Umpqua, following it toward the source instead of toward the sea, and he arranged to have one of Centrenose's sons accompany him on the expedition.

On October 23, taking one horse for his guide to use and one to carry his supplies, he started out on foot. After a stop at Centrenose's lodge where he again found the Indians friendly and helpful, he traveled on toward the east. Bad weather and lack of food plagued him. On

the night of the twenty-fifth, he was caught in one of
the worst storms he had ever experienced. Violent rain
drenched his campfire. At midnight his tent was blown
down. While he tried to sleep, rolled in a wet blanket,
the two terrified horses sought his protection and stood
with their heads hanging over him, neighing mournfully.

He was still shivering from the cold when he started
out the next morning. Worse, his head ached severely,
there were pains in his stomach, and he experienced a
fit of giddiness and dimness of sight that almost forced
him to remain where he was. He had only a few grains of
calomel for medicine. Saving that for some greater emer-
gency, he exercised until he was perspiring violently.
That evening, after traveling eighteen miles and having
eaten some fish he had obtained from Indians on the
south side of the river, he felt a little better.

In the morning he left his camp at daylight, telling
his guide to stay in camp and dry out the papers used
for wrapping plant specimens. About an hour's walk
from the camp, Douglas was surprised by a tall, naked
Indian, his face marked with red earth, his eyes sparked
with fear.

Immediately, the Indian strung his bow and placed
a sleeve of raccoon skin on his left arm to protect his
flesh from arrow burn.

Douglas stood still, knowing that a false move would bring an arrow singing through his chest. Undoubtedly the Indian had never seen a white man before and fear was his only reaction.

"Stay close," Douglas whispered to Billy. He laid his gun at his feet and beckoned to the native.

Cautiously, slowly, the Indian approached. When he was near, Douglas managed to persuade him to lay down his bow and arrow beside the gun. Then he struck a light to his pipe and offered it to the Indian, along with some beads.

When the Indian accepted his gifts, Douglas relaxed and tried to question the man about the great pine. He made a rough sketch of the tree as he imagined it to look, pointed at the drawing, then at himself.

"*Natele?*" the Indian said. Raising a bronze, muscular arm he pointed to some hills about twenty miles to the south.

Douglas' pulse quickened. He picked up his gun, careful to do it in such a way that he would not alarm the Indian, and started off. He was really on the trail at last. The Indian watched him in silence for a moment, then to Douglas' surprise, followed him.

The sun was at its high point, shining feebly through the clouds, when Douglas reached the hills. He caught sight of the distant tops of the conifers and walked more quickly. Some of the trees rose over two hundred feet in the air! As he came closer, he saw overhanging branches drooping heavily from the upper third of the trunks. Here were the trees, their great cones hanging from the tips of the branches like small sugar loaves in a grocer's shop. His long-sought pine at last!

Indifferent to the watching Indian, he went to the nearest tree and stretched his arms around its rich, purple-brown trunk, estimating its girth. As he drew away —his arms having gone only part way around its rough circumference—he saw that he had pressed his cheek against glazed, sugary sap that had oozed out. Tasting the sap he found it as sweet as sugar.

The Indian broke off some of the glittering beads and licked them, also.

A sugar pine, Douglas thought, craning his neck to stare upward at the crest of one of the trees. Now that he had found it, the problem of obtaining the cones was as great as it had been with the first mighty conifer he had sought. This time, however, he had a rifle with a longer range. With luck, he might be able to clip off some of the high boughs.

He began shooting at the high branches. There, the tip of one bough came tumbling down, bearing a rich cone with it. He tried again. After a series of shots he had three plump, seed-ripe cones. Elated, he raised his gun again.

Brush rustled behind him. Billy growled. Douglas turned. Staring at him in sullen, suspicious silence stood eight Indians. All were painted with red earth and heavily armed with bows and arrows, bone spears, and flint knives. They exchanged a few guttural words with the first Indian, eyeing Douglas all the while.

Douglas stepped forward, laid down his gun again, making signs of friendship. He offered his pipe. After a brief hesitation, the Indians sat down with him and smoked, apparently prepared to be peaceful.

Just as Douglas felt some of his tension lessen, he saw one of the Indians stringing his bow. Another began sharpening his flint knife which he then hung on his right wrist. There was no mistaking their intentions. Douglas sent a glance of appeal to the Indian who had accompanied him here, but either he was powerless to help or he did not want to. He sat silent.

There was no hope of flight. Even Billy would be hard put to it to outrun the savages on his short legs. Douglas realized he would have to get out of this situation by a bold display of courage, if he could get out at all.

Douglas got to his feet quickly, stepped back six paces, and cocked his gun, taking the Indians by surprise. With his left hand he whipped his pistol from his belt.

One of the Indians started toward him, then thought better of it and stayed where he was.

A minute went by. Another minute. Still Douglas stood aiming both barrels at the crew, praying that they would not risk a battle. Three minutes. There was complete silence. Douglas could hear the ticking of his watch in his vest pocket, keeping time with the rapid beating of his heart. Four minutes. Five. He was glad the Indians could not see the sweat running down his back. Six. Seven. He had not realized how heavy his pistol was before. An ache spread into his wrist. Many more minutes and he would be forced to lower the weapon. Eight . . .

One of the Indians, apparently the leader, suddenly held up his hand, making the sign for tobacco.

Warily, Douglas lowered his pistol and pushed it back in his belt, but he kept his gun in hand. Gesturing and "talking" with his left hand, he indicated to the Indians that they would get some tobacco if they would go and bring him more pine cones.

Rubbing their bellies in anticipation of European

tobacco, they nodded and made signs of agreement and trotted off.

Douglas waited until they were out of sight. Then, taking time only to gather the three cones he had shot down, and a few twigs, he fled from the spot. Every other minute he thought he heard the Indians pursuing him although he weaved back and forth on his trail in an effort to confuse them in case they were following him. Once, when Billy barked at a hoary marmot that popped up out of its hole, Douglas silenced him by clamping a hand around the terrier's bearded muzzle. "Save your barking for Scotland!" he said.

Breathless and shaken, Douglas arrived at his camp. There the young Indian guide was peacefully drying the botanical papers as he had been instructed to do. He looked at Douglas' tense face in curiosity and Douglas attempted to explain something of what had happened. But it was too hard to make him understand through the barrier of a different language, and he gave up.

That night as he lay on the grass, writing in his journal with the aid of a burning "Columbia candle," a piece of wood containing rosin, Douglas' mood wavered between triumph over the end of his long quest and nervous apprehension over a stealthy attack. His gun was close at his side, ready for action.

His Indian guide snored peacefully. With a sigh,
Douglas closed his journal, blew out his candle and
stared up at the cloud-dimmed stars. How many, many
nights he had lain like this, unable to talk to someone
who would understand, lacking a book or anything else
to read. He felt starved for the companionship of fellow
scientists.

One hand closed on Billy's rough fur. For all that
Billy was the most faithful of companions, he had his
limits. Where was John Scouler now? he wondered.
And was Hooker, perhaps, on one of his Highland
rambles, looking up at this same sky?

The wilderness answered none of his questions. From
a nearby tree an owl screeched solemnly. A flying
squirrel made a slight thud as it landed against a branch.

Douglas turned over, closing his eyes, trusting Billy
to wake him if there were danger. He had chosen this
lonely life, this grueling search for the green beauty
of the earth. Yes, and he could think of none other with
half the adventure or the reward. Perhaps the quest
had chosen him. Sleepily he remembered the ripe and
splendid cones of the sugar pine. They grew in his mind,
and in his dreams the pine incense mingled with the odor
of his smoking candle.

Chapter Nine

Up the Rockies

Grouse sang in the woods, the male birds making a melancholy "hurr-r-r-hoo, hurr-r-r-rhoo" sound as they did their springtime courting. Douglas listened both with pleasure and an answering melancholy. The long winter was over and even the new year of 1827 that had been ushered in by the firing of cannon at Fort Vancouver was now three months old. March had come again with its new buds and shoots and sweet-smelling winds. March and the end of Douglas' two years of travels and search in the wilderness region of the Columbia.

As he packed his gear in preparation for traveling with the Hudson's Bay express across the continent, he felt torn between the joy of returning to England and Scotland and sadness at saying farewell to the woods and streams he had come to love. Hunting out some of the Indians and giving them farewell gifts, he realized he would miss them, too.

He would not have to tell Dr. McLoughlin and others of the Company goodbye yet for they would travel as far as Fort Colville with the express.

Douglas looked over the piles of seeds, cones, twigs, plants, stuffed birds, animal skulls, mosses and rocks he had gathered. He could not relax until they were safe in Sabine's hands.

The next morning, March 20, Douglas set out with the Company's flat-bottomed express boat and one smaller boat. At every opportunity he went on shore to hunt for plants. He shot a male grouse as a specimen to take back to England. Later, he shot a female grouse. Each bird went into the sack on his back. When he reached Fort Colville, he had carried the cock 457 miles, the hen 304. At the fort he tied the birds in oilcloth and hung them from the poles of his tent.

Returning from a brief side trip into the woods, Douglas arrived just as two of the Indians' dogs were finishing the grouse. They had managed to get the bag down, had eaten through the leather thongs around the oilcloth, and had devoured feathers and all.

Billy rushed forward, ready for a fight. One of the

starving hounds snarled, then turned tail and fled, followed by his companion.

Douglas stared bitterly at the remains of the birds he had packed on his back for so many miles. Looking at the seed parcels inside the tent, he observed to Billy: "It's a good thing for botany that the Indian dogs aren't vegetarians or we'd not have a seed left to take home."

He was still grieving about his lost grouse the next morning when he finally told Dr. McLoughlin goodbye. He gripped the doctor's hand and tried to express his gratitude for all that the White-headed Eagle had done.

"You'll always be welcome at Fort Vancouver," McLoughlin answered, "if you come back. And perhaps you will."

"Perhaps," Douglas said.

"Ready, Douglas?" called Francis Ermatinger, the young commander of the brigade heading for Hudson's Bay.

"Ready," Douglas said.

Soon he was on his way northward with Ermatinger, four Canadians, and three Iroquois Indians—on toward Arrow Lakes and the Dalles des Morts ("Rapids of Death"), Athabaska Pass in the northern Rockies, and the North Saskatchewan River. New territories. New fields for botany. Even as he waved to the men on shore, his thoughts leaped ahead far in advance of the boat slicing the waters of the Columbia.

Each day there was magnificent scenery to watch. Snow-tipped mountains adorned with dark pines, the silver-white foam of the river. Douglas tried to describe the beauty in his journal but he felt his words were mere shadows of what he saw. He resolved that when he got home he would master the art of words. Especially in the evenings, his surroundings tugged at his emotions. The ragged firelight. The sound of Ermatinger's flute blending with the forest noises. The dim silhouettes of the Selkirk Mountains. Or, when at dusk they paddled through narrow cliffs where the river became a gloomy path of shadow through dark masses of granite and torn trees, the savage splendor brought him a feeling of awe that was close to horror.

At the dangerous Dalles des Morts, he saw the graves of earlier adventurers who had perished one by one in the impenetrable forests around the rapids.

When they reached the head of the Big Bend of the Columbia, Douglas got his first glimpse of the Rockies. If his pen had failed before, it was doubly at a loss now.

On leaving the sturdy express boat at Boat Encampment at the Big Bend of the Columbia River, Douglas computed the number of miles he had traveled on and about the mighty stream. In all, he had traveled seven thousand miles.

The group crossed Athabaska Pass on foot. Ermatinger offered to have Douglas' supplies carried by others in the party but Douglas declined. The rest were already heavily laden. Strapping his forty-three-pound sack on his back, he trudged on.

On the first day, a three-mile swamp had to be crossed. Douglas often sank to his knees in the cold mire. Even Billy, light though he was, sometimes went in up to his belly. In the woods on the other side, snowdrifts from four to seven feet high gave them more trouble. Douglas strapped on a pair of snowshows called "bearpaws" because of their round, paw-like shape, and struggled to master them. The laces got wet, came loose, and tripped him. Others fell, too, as their snowshoes tangled with the underbrush.

Fourteen times in one day, the nine men crossed the winding Wood River. As Douglas plunged into the freezing water to his waist, he urged the shivering Billy to swim close at his side. The river water was not only cold but treacherous, the currents dragging at the men's feet so that they often had to form a chain by holding each other's hands. Douglas fastened a rope around Billy to keep him from being washed away.

Between swamps and drifts, rivers and brushwood, Douglas still found the time and energy to collect bird and plant specimens, though each scrap of treasure added more weight to his already heavy sack. The lacings of his snowshoes made his ankles swell. He made a pair of toeless socks from the legs of an old pair of stockings and cut off the wide hem of his coat to wrap around his toes.

The land began to go more steeply upward, the snow became deeper, the gullies and ravines creating tremendous gaps for the travelers to circumvent. Douglas found himself ascending two steps and sliding back three. When his snowshoes twisted and tossed him to earth, he confessed to Ermatinger: "I feel like a broken-down wagon horse entangled in its harness, weltering to rescue myself."

Bedding down in the snow near Athabaska Pass, Douglas dreamed that he was walking along Regent Street in London. When he awoke it seemed that the dream was real and this wild and mountain-dominated landscape must be the dream. The pangs of hunger were real enough, however, for food was increasingly scarce.

When Ermatinger shot a plump grouse to add to the larder, there were cries of approval from the voyageurs. Douglas joined in, his mouth watering—before he got a closer look at the bird.

"Wait, Ermatinger!" he said, taking the grouse from him. "Look at that plumage, man. It's too beautiful a creature to eat."

"Beauty!" a voyageur scoffed. "Who can live on beauty?"

But Douglas persisted. He would not sacrifice such a splendid bird to the kettle. "I'll go without my share of the supper," he declared. Getting the resolute look to his face that indicated opposition was useless, he proceeded to preserve the bird as a specimen. As he worked with cold-chilled fingers, he had no way of knowing that the Franklin Grouse would be on display in the Royal Scottish Museum one hundred and thirty years later, a feathered witness to his persistence and skill.

Nor could he know that another exploit that he undertook near the summit of the pass would result in an error being printed on maps and in geography books for many years after.

From the moment Douglas had seen the mighty peaks of the Rockies he had wanted to climb them. Now, on May 1, the express was camped directly below the summit of the great range. On the left, a giant peak rose into the air, seeming at his elbow. Putting on his snowshoes and taking a small collecting box, he started off, this time without Billy.

At the beginning, pines and snowdrifts accompanied him, but halfway to the summit the pines and vegetation ceased. Nothing but bare rocks and snow greeted his searching gaze. The snow firmed to a hard crust so that for a time climbing was easier. Then, two-thirds of the way to the summit, the snow hardened to ice. Skidding, sometimes crawling, Douglas continued upward, his eyes half-shut against the blue-gray glare. The silence was so thick that when one lonely blue jay gave its hoarse call, the sound startled him.

After five hours Douglas reached the summit, the first man ever to ascend any of the northern Rockies. As far as he could see were mountains, their slopes covered with sky-tinted snows, azure glaciers, rainbow-hued boulders, huge mossy icicles hanging from steep rocks where avalanches of snow went sliding and smashing downward to crash against other rocks below.

For twenty minutes Douglas stayed on the peak. He tried to estimate its height. It surely was the highest. Another peak, southward, rose nearly as high. Considering how the vegetation had given out around 5,000 feet, with 1200 feet of ice beyond, he calculated that the peak he had climbed must be about 16,000 feet above the sea. The other, almost the same height, he estimated at 15,700 feet.

Mighty peaks should bear mighty names, he decided. He christened the eminence on which he stood "Mt. Brown," in honor of the distinguished English botanist, Robert Brown. The other sunset-shining peak he named "Mt. Hooker" for his beloved friend and teacher, William Hooker.

Dusk was pouring dark shadows into the valleys and ravines and he had to make his descent. Going down over the ice sheet was different from climbing it. He slid more often than he stayed upright. Braking himself against a rock, he remembered that he had only one pair of trousers to last him through the rest of the journey. He took off his shoes, tied them together, and placed them under him to serve as a sled. As he shot downwards he felt the thrill of speed. But when he reached the woods again he paused in the dusk long enough to investigate crowberries hidden under the snow, the dead stems of gentians, and a tiny primrose which in time to come would be called the *Snow douglasia* after him.

For more than sixty years, Douglas' estimates of the heights of the two mountains stood, giving Mt. Brown the title of the highest mountain on the North American continent. When accurate measurements were finally made, Mt. Brown's altitude dwindled to a little over 9,000 feet, and Mt. Hooker to close to 11,000. Between the time of Douglas' ascent and the final, official measurements of the peaks, controversy raged and Douglas was accused of deliberately misrepresenting the heights.

Douglas was unaware of anything but the present as he made his way back to camp. Without any mountaineering equipment, he had just put two mountains on the map. Luckily, he thought with a grin, he didn't have to add them to his knapsack.

The worst of the journey was behind, once the summit was crossed. On the eastern side of the Rockies, horses were obtained. Then, turning to boats again, the party proceeded up the Athabaska River to Jasper House, an establishment built by the Northwest Fur Company.

From there they traveled east to Fort Edmonton where John Rowand, the Chief Factor, gave Douglas a young golden eagle. Although the Indian boys around the fort had plucked some of the eagle's tail feathers for decorating war caps, the bird was an excellent specimen. With some difficulty, Douglas got the fierce bird into a cage.

At Fort Edmonton, too, other Company traders joined the party, among them Finan McDonald. On the first day of June, as they traveled through buffalo country, McDonald and several other men went out at dawn to

hunt the shaggy brown beasts. Douglas did his own kind
of hunting, cramming seeds into his sack. He had returned to camp to unload his specimens, well satisfied,
and was setting out again when he heard a commotion
on the other side of the North Saskatchewan River. A
boat was putting out and Douglas ran down to it. One of
the men explained, "Ermatinger and Herriot got two
buffaloes. We're going across to get the meat."

When they reached the other shore Douglas learned
that McDonald had been wounded. He lay on the ground,
his huge body bleeding from many wounds.

"Gored by a wounded bull," a trapper said as Douglas
came near. "We thought he was dead."

Douglas became aware that all the men were looking
toward him for help. Plant science and medical science
were entirely different things, he thought, feeling
helpless as he inspected McDonald. Still, he always
carried a lancet. He took it out, and in spite of all the
blood McDonald had already lost, bled him some more.
That done, he bound up his wounds and forced twenty-
five drops of laudanum down McDonald's throat to put
him to sleep.

During the five days it took for the party to take
McDonald to the next post around three hundred miles
away, the big trader's life seesawed in the balance. When

he was strong enough to grip Douglas' hand, he said with a wry smile, "I can't say whether I recovered in spite of ye, Douglas, or because of ye, but I'm thankful."

Day after day the group pushed eastward. They reached Lake Winnipeg, crossed it, and finally arrived at Norway House, the crossroads of the northland. There, Douglas found mail, including a letter from Sabine. With joyous relief, he read Sabine's phrases of satisfaction with what he had done, even to extending his time on the Columbia for a year.

His pleasure was blotted out, however, as the letter went on to say that his father had died. His brother John's letter held the same sad news.

As the express traveled on, Douglas crammed even more botanical activity into his spare moments, to keep from grieving over his father. Only when he finally saw the Company's ship, the *Prince of Wales,* riding at anchor on Hudson's Bay did his spirits lighten. The ship was his transportation to England.

His spirits plunged again, however, when the golden eagle he had treasured entangled itself in its leash and strangled to death. Sadly, he wrote in his journal, "What can give one more pain? This animal I carried 2,000 miles and now lost him, I might say, at home."

But he was not yet home. While waiting for the ship to

leave, Douglas and some fellow scientists, who were returning home after an Arctic expedition with Captain John Franklin, went in a boat with eight oarsmen to pay a visit to the ship out in the bay. As they returned in the evening a strong wind arose, reaching hurricane proportions in a few minutes. Waves all but tore the oars from the men's hands and, bobbing helplessly, the boat was swept out to sea. Waves broke over the sides until the boat threatened to sink.

"Bail!" one of the men cried.

"With what?" someone asked.

One of the scientists took off his hat and scooped it into the water and the others imitated him. Douglas felt the wind and rain tear at his hair. He wondered wryly how the small bald spot starting at the top of his skull would fare—he would be lucky to have any hair left.

Night came on with the howling wind. Night and bitter cold. Numbness gripped Douglas' arms so that he could scarcely continue bailing.

When dawn light finally appeared, the wind still blasted the water and there was no sign of land. The oarsmen tried again to use the oars but it was hopeless.

All day the boat pitched helplessly in the continuing storm. All day Douglas and the others bailed. He began to feel nausea. When darkness came once more, he wondered if he would live to feel warmth or softness or light again.

In the middle of the second night, the wind slackened. The men began to row in what they hoped was the right direction. After seventy miles of back-breaking effort, they reached shore and staggered toward shelter. Men stared in awe for everyone had given them up for dead.

When the *Prince of Wales* sailed on September 15, Douglas was not on deck to take a farewell glimpse of the great bay and York Factory with its warehouses and smithy and carpenter shop grouped within its palisades. He lay ill in his bunk, scarcely able to move his limbs. He said a silent farewell to the land that had brought him so much physical suffering and so many botanical triumphs. He heard the anchor rattling upward and the northwest wind from the Barren Lands striking the sails. Billy gave a low, sorrowful whine.

He patted the dog's head. "We'll find another adventure, Billy," he said hoarsely. "And more green treasure. Enough to girdle the globe."

For the moment he was content to lie still, his worn-out body rocking with the tilt and sway of the boat, Billy warm against his side.

Chapter Ten

The Cage

Douglas, just home from London, sat in what had been his father's chair, his feet toasting on the fireplace hearth. Through the window he could see the evening mist gathering in the hollows and hanging in thin veils around the outbuildings. Near the barn stood the old crates and cages that had once held his pet owls and eagles. They were weather-scoured and forlorn-looking and he was half-tempted to climb Kinnoul Hill for new specimens to destroy the sense of emptiness the cages gave him. The cottage itself seemed empty now with so many of the family gone. John had come down with him from London, but except for their mother and their youngest sister who was visiting a sick neighbor, the rest were gone. Even George, the "bairn," was now working for a potter in Staffordshire. Douglas sighed and lifted his teacup.

153

"Is the tay hot enough, Davy?" his mother asked from her chair, her knitting needles clicking rhythmically.

Behind her, John laughed softly. "That's the third time you've asked him that. Don't forget he's an expert at making his own tea now, and over a wilderness campfire, at that." John stood with his back to the hearth, his fashionable frock coat and spotless linen in keeping with his position as a successful young architect.

"It's the best tea in Perth," Douglas answered his mother. "Next time I go traveling I'm going to arrange to take you along to be my cook."

"Next time?" His mother looked up, concern wrinkling her forehead. "You want to go and kill yoursel' truly next time instead of doing half a job?"

He had been ill for weeks after the ship had reached England, unable to read to the Linnean Society the paper he had written on the sugar pine. Sabine had read the manuscript for him. And even after he was up and around, moments of giddiness and dimness of sight plagued him.

John challenged his mother, "You don't think you can keep him home for good now, do you, after a year's diet of fame?" Mocking the voice and gestures of an orator, John proclaimed: "David Douglas, Esquire, Fellow of the Linnean Society which numbers among its eminent members the leading scientists of the world! Fellow of the Zoological Society of London! Fellow of the Geological Society. Recipient of decorations and honors, from the cliffs of Dover to the Highlands—and from the kings and queens of Russia, Denmark, the Netherlands . . ."

Douglas whirled in his chair, his face flushed, the teacup in his hand sloshing its contents onto his knee. "What good is it all if I'm to be stuck in London for the rest of my life, breathing in smoke and grime? Is that the Society's reward for my bringing back more new plants and seeds than any man ever did before?"

"Mind your tongue with your brother, Davy!" his mother spoke up. "Take your peevishness out on your London friends, if you must."

"That's all right, Mother," John said. "I can protect myself from this savage." He sat down on the stool across from David, half-bantering, half-earnest. "Come on now, David. You know you liked all the fanfare. In fact, I heard some say that it had turned your head."

David sniffed scornfully. "Fame! I'd give it to the first Indian I met in the woods."

In spite of his denial, Douglas secretly admitted that there was some truth in John's words. At first, being courted and complimented and admired everywhere, his travels and botanical articles featured in leading publications, he felt that he had reached the peak of his ambition. What more, he had wondered, could a young man want? Aye, his head had been turned a bit. But only for a bit. Now fame seemed as empty as those cages out there and all he had to look forward to was a post as a curator in some public or private garden, unless he went on forever puttering in the Royal Horticultural Society's garden where so many of his wilderness plants were now installed.

He got up restlessly and paced around the small quarters. "I didn't mean to speak so sharp, but my nerves are honed like a razor."

John nodded. "Almost all your friends in London are aware of that by now. You'd better forget about going off to some foreign land, brother. If the Society doesn't need any more such collecting for awhile, that's that. You did too good a job. If you hadn't brought a regular mountain of seeds and plants—"

"And skins of birds and animals," David broke in, "that they let rot unpacked! I didn't burn and freeze and get wet to the skin to bring specimens home for the moths to eat."

"The Society's been more than good to you," Mrs. Douglas said. "Sulking and being disagreeable to others

will get you nowhere. Sit, Davy, and drink your tea. I
don't like that hoarseness in your voice. You'd better
let me rub your throat and chest with hot goose grease
tonight."

David started to protest, then shrugged and sat down.
It was no use repeating that the colds and sore throat
he had suffered from so often in the year since he had
returned from America were the result of the black
fumes and smoke and ashy air of London. "The London
climate kills me," he had told Prof. Hooker. Goose
grease was no cure for a sickness that was growing more
crucial every day, a sickness of spirit that put a blight on
everything. Like mildew on plants, he thought bleakly.
He would say no more in criticism of the Society. It
and Sabine were being criticized enough by others.

"Goose grease it is, then, Mother," he said.

"And a bit of grease for his tongue, too," John said
with a sly grin, "to get the snap out of it."

"The proper thing," Douglas said, leaning back in
his chair and staring at the red embers of the fire dream-
ily, "would be a sweat bath like the Chinooks use. They
dig a hole, put hot stones in, and pour water over the
stones to make steam. Then, naked, an Indian goes in,
works up a fine sweat, and thereupon plunges into the
river. Once I saw a big Chinook . . . "

John and Mrs. Douglas listened as David launched

into yet another story of his wilderness travels. These moments when he relived his Columbia River adventures were the only ones in which he really appeared to relax.

As he talked, he fancied he could hear the wind of the great pines over him, and the harsh whispers of the river. What were Chief Concomly and Dr. McLoughlin and Young Wasp and Francis Ermatinger doing now? Were they lugging a canoe over the rocks of a portage, or roasting a big salmon over the fire?

"Those pines," he murmured. "The *Pinus taxifolia* —the first of the great pines I saw from shipboard—" His eyes lit up. "Sabine said last week that it should be called the *Pinus douglasii*—after me! What do you think of that now? Perhaps when he puts out a new edition of Lambert's work on the pines, he'll change the old name." He drew himself up, eyeing his family challengingly. "How is that for a lad who couldn't be kept in school?"

His mother looked at him. "Are you boasting now?"

"Well, it's no small thing to have a great tree named after one," David defended himself.

"And no little thing to carry the name of Douglas, either. The Douglas men have always been modest."

John put a hand on David's shoulder. "He has a right

to be proud, Mother. Only he shouldn't pretend that fame tastes like bitters to him."

"It's no pretense," David retorted, the sharpness back in his voice. "I'd trade it all for a field of growing grass."

"Maybe you'll get your growing grass," John said. "The Society may decide to send you somewhere just to be rid of you."

There was a scratching at the door.

"It's Billy," David said and got up. "He wants to sleep under the blanket with me for the night."

"You'll have to choose between me and him," John said. "I'm not sharing the bed with a dog."

"You can keep your bed," David answered curtly. "Billy and I will curl up under the stars."

Mrs. Douglas got up. "You're in a civilized country now, Davy, and you'll sleep as all decent folk do, in bed. And Billy will sleep by the hearth like a civilized dog."

Douglas did not argue but he smiled to himself and at Billy. "D'you hear, laddie? On the hearth with you. Down. That's right."

John looked at Billy doubtfully. "How about a stout rope . . . ?"

"He'd be humiliated. I'll ha' you know he's a most obedient dog." His good humor returned and he added, grinning, "I've no doubt Sabine will be naming some plant after Billy before all's said and done."

The brothers went off to the rear of the cottage where the bed they had shared as boys was made up for them. As Douglas crawled between the clean, coarse sheets and heard the straw rustle in the tick, he wondered if he would ever again grow accustomed to the softness of regular beds. But he was weary enough after the jolting stage ride from London to sleep almost anywhere.

Sleepily he answered John's scraps of conversation until John dozed off. He closed his eyes but sleep did not come. His thoughts began going in familiar circles: he must learn to resign himself to being a gardener in England the rest of his life, if that was what was in store for him. A man had to adapt himself to circumstances and there were far worse things than a peaceful, successful life as a gardener. Money was nothing to him. As for fame—well, he had had a full taste of that. And if the great fir were named after him, that would be an immortal reward.

His thoughts went back to the night years ago when William Beattie had come to this house and offered him an apprentice's job in the Scone gardens. He remembered how he had dreamed of some plant or bush or tree bearing his name. Big dreams, he had thought then. Still, in order to accomplish great things one must have great dreams and hopes. Startled, he realized that almost those same words had gone through his mind on that other night so long ago.

Were they true or just an excuse for impatience and unreasonable ambition?

If a man were content with little, he would have and do little. This he felt sure of. If he went searching for no more than a handful of plants, that is all he would return with. But if he went after a mountain, he might return with the globe itself. Mentally he reached out, seeming to feel the dark earth spinning in his cupped hands, the fruits and flowers, the thorns and blossoms, pricking his palms.

Something plopped onto the bed—something gray and warm and wet-tongued.

Douglas pulled Billy beside him, whispering, "Sh-h-h! You're welcome for the night, if you're quiet, but before the sun's up you'd better be back by the hearth or we'll have the mist for a bed tomorrow night."

Billy trembled with pleasure and snuggled down.

"And no snores!" Douglas admonished. His eyelids sagged. Just before he dropped into heavy slumber, his right hand pawed at the blanket for his absent gun.

Douglas returned to London determined to accept in good grace whatever fate brought him. But in a few

days, exposed to the bustle and grime and monotony
of the city, his spirits became "mildewed" again. Even
visits with Hooker in Glasgow, or with Archibald Menzies and Thomas Nuttall and other botanists, did not
compensate for his feeling of loss. He grew more dis-
gruntled and unhappy, even neglecting his clothing so
that at times he looked the shabby wilderness walker he
yearned to be.

He appealed to Sabine, "Do you not remember how
you urged me to study Spanish? I did study it. Now
where am I to use it? Talking to the flowers in the garden? There is all of California to explore yet."

"True," Sabine said. "But we've had reports that the
savages are too ferocious. We don't want to risk your
neck, Douglas, even for more plants."

"All my neck's good for now is for holding my head
up," Douglas answered.

He knew that he was giving in to his old impatience,
so much so that even Hooker was becoming critical. A
visit from Hooker in the spring of 1829 resulted in
Hooker's giving him a kindly lecture on the virtues of
patience and restraint. For a time Douglas struggled
again to be content, arranging the herbarium, nursing
along the garden plants, working at his journal. Also, a
faint hope stirred his heart. Hooker, for one, believed
that Douglas should be sent out into the field again and

he used his influence with Sabine and others in positions of control.

"Anyhow," Hooker told Sabine, "Douglas will never give up pestering you until you arrange another journey for him. If the secret of success is constancy of purpose, Douglas is bound to be successful."

"Constancy of purpose or stubbornness?" Sabine asked.

"The proof is in the eating." Hooker laughed. "And a wild pudding he is."

Stubborn or resolute, impatient or merely determined, Douglas strained toward his one goal by every look, action, and thought—and in July of that year, 1829, the Society surrendered.

The minutes of the Council stated that David Douglas was to be sent once more, to the western part of North America, with the assistance of the Hudson's Bay Company and the Colonial Office, to explore all the territory west of the Rocky Mountains from California northward as far as he was able to go. Chiefly, however, he was to explore the interior of California in search of botanical treasures. He was scheduled to depart on September 15 on a Hudson's Bay Company ship, the *Eagle*.

Douglas felt like a plant which has been imprisoned in shade and then suddenly transplanted into sunlight. Even the smoke-charged air of London seemed bright and dazzling. Feverishly he plunged into preparations for his new journey. This time, he resolved, he would be better equipped than he had been before. With the help of Sabine's brother, who was secretary to the great scientific organization, the Royal Society, he applied himself to the subject he had hated at school: arithmetic. Not just arithmetic but trigonometry and logarithms in conjunction with instruments for establishing geographical positions: the sextant, the compass, chronometer, hygrometer, and others.

Hour after hour, often for eighteen hours a day, Douglas pored over his study books and charts. The snow-blindness and inflammation of the eyeball that had tormented him on the Columbia had left his vision so impaired that he could not read small type or figures. The old Bible that he had carried with him through heat and cold blurred as he tried to read it and he wrote to Hooker asking him to find a Bible with large type in Glasgow.

Over-excitement and overwork brought on a siege of illness, too, so that he was forced to spend a short time in bed before traveling back to Scone to tell his mother goodbye.

His mother's eyes were dry but her voice was sad as she stroked his cheek and admonished him, "Son, take care, take care. The trees will grow and the birds sing whether you find them or not."

He smiled, his arm around her. "Aye, Mother, but perhaps they will not grow so fast nor sing so well. And certainly they will not grow and sing in England or here among the braes and glens if I do not bring them back."

"Bring yourself back, lad. And your Billy. He can ha' his own wee bed next time."

The hills were behind her when Douglas left, walking the road to Scone—great, green mounds they were, that made her seem frail and lonely and lost. Douglas swallowed a lump in his throat. When would he see her or these hills of home again, he wondered?

Mist covered the sun entirely and the landscape darkened. He stared ahead into the unknown. For two years he had bent every effort toward attaining the goal of departure. Now something in him drew back, but just for an instant.

Fort Vancouver again! The Walla Walla. Perhaps the Blue Mountains once more. Old friends. And then the new land, California, land of Spanish missions and golden sunlight. Ferocious savages, too, Sabine had warned.

Savages? Rather, new friends! Dust churned around his shoes and settled softly on the roadside heather as he walked faster, eager to be on his way.

Chapter Eleven

El Camino Real

California sunlight flickered through the open door of the adobe fort at Monterey, glistening on a row of ants marching across the earth floor. David Douglas, seated across from the new governor of California, Manuel Victoria, heard the muffled noise of the Mexican soldiers drilling on the presidio grounds. From what he had seen of their military drills, the ants were far more orderly. As for the fortifications, they were nothing more than a mud wall with three sides, a breastwork about three feet high, and seven guns mounted on platforms so rotten that even the ants had to walk over them with care.

Two of the ants set out on patrol toward Victoria's dusty boot while the main body of the insect army began scaling the leg of the rough table where the Governor was signing his name to a piece of paper.

Douglas waited impatiently. There had been delays all along the line. He had not sailed from England until October, 1829. Then there was time spent in Honolulu so that he did not arrive at the Columbia until June of the next year, where he had spent six months. Four more months had passed since his arrival at the Monterey harbor in December.

The Governor hesitated in mid-signature. "Another thing, señor," he said to Douglas in Spanish, "you must promise not to make any drawings of our fortifications. The new republic of Mexico has many enemies and we must take all precautions."

Douglas promised solemnly, repeating that his only desire was to study the flora and fauna of the country. He had already had many interviews with Victoria—*El Gobernador Negro*, the Black Governor, as the citizens called him because of his dark complexion. The swarthy soldier was eternally suspicious. Confusion and conflict, from Mexico itself to the territory of California, were rampant since Mexico had revolted against Spain ten years before and set up as an independent republic.

Victoria took his pen again and completed his signature on Douglas' passport. He held it out to him. "It is yours. For six months only—and not even six hours if there is trouble."

Douglas glanced over the document. *"Abril 20—Carta de Seguridad de David Duglas . . . "* His name was misspelled, he saw, but he decided that it was better not to mention it. Thanking the Governor, and making a crude imitation of a Spanish bow, he left, the precious scrap of paper in his coat pocket. Permission to stay and travel for six months. So little time for such a vast territory.

Billy, waiting by the door, trotted at Douglas' heels along the rough street. Douglas looked around at the forests spreading for miles in every direction beyond the village of Monterey, the hills thick with pine and live oaks. In the kelp beds off shore, glossy sea otters floated serenely on their backs, nibbling at shellfish. On the rocks, sea lions barked or roared. Southward on the peninsula were the magnificent Del Monte woods. Douglas had already rambled through those woods, and around the bay to Santa Cruz where he had seen the great redwood trees, the mighty *Sequoia sempervirens*, that grew north of the mission there.

The bells of the San Carlos mission rang out, summoning the Indian workers from the fields and vineyards. Douglas went on toward the home of William Hartnell, an English merchant who had married a Spanish señorita and settled there.

It was a joy to Douglas to be able to talk in English with one of his own countrymen. That evening, resting in the light of the tallow candles in Hartnell's parlor, he told his host that he was at last free to explore.

"We'll miss your company, *Don* Douglas," Hartnell said. "However, I think your travels will be easier than on the Columbia. Most of the highway between the missions is little more than a horse trail but down south you'll find oxcarts and *carretas* traveling along with you."

"Yes, it's a far cry from the Columbia," Douglas agreed.

Still, he reflected, Fort Vancouver was not the primitive outpost it had been at the time of his first visit. When he had landed at Fort Vancouver last June, before coming on to California, he had been astonished to find the changes that had occurred there while he was in England. Dr. McLoughlin had moved the fort to higher ground closer to the river. The herds of cattle had doubled in size. The gardens and farmlands were rich with plants and crops, and the buildings were improved. There were new faces at the fort, too, boys from the Greenwich Naval School who were to be trained for the Hudson's Bay Company's coast service. Unchanging and unchanged were the vast botanical riches in the

Columbia district—riches that gave him a hundred new species to send back to Sabine, plus three large chests of seeds which included another new pine.

"Between Ventura and Santa Barbara," Hartnell was saying, "you may have to ride your horse right into the surf, if you pass at high tide."

Douglas shook his head and smiled, leaning down to pat Billy. "I'll be walking on my own feet. A horse adds to the expense, not to mention that a botanist needs to keep his nose as close to the ground as possible." He stood up as Señora Hartnell came into the room. If ever he lost his heart, he thought, it would be to a woman like Hartnell's wife, a dark-haired señorita of California.

Señora Hartnell expressed her sadness at his departure, and repeated the traditional words of hospitality, in Spanish: *"Mi casa es suya.* My house is yours."

Later, Douglas followed the Indian servant up to his bedchamber. There, Billy beside him, he watched the stars glide over the Gabilan Range to the east. He drew up a mental itinerary for the future: Soledad, San Antonio, San Miguel, San Luis Obispo, Santa Barbara.

Down in the dark street, a soldier was strumming a guitar. Now and then the guttural voice of an Indian floated up, contrasting to the soft voices speaking in Spanish.

"Good night, Señor Billy," Douglas said at last. "Tomorrow another journey."

As Hartnell had said, *El Camino Real*, the Royal Road, was little better than a horse trail. Still, it was a trail, and Douglas and Billy had no trouble following it from one resting place to another. The missions built by the Spanish were about one day's foot journey apart. But Douglas' journeying was not that of an ordinary traveler trying to reach a destination by nightfall. He left the trail more often than he stayed on it, scrambling up the slopes of hills, thrashing through brush, crossing occasional streams. On the summits of hills he got out his instruments for measuring latitudes and longitudes, collecting geographic data along with flowers and seeds.

Away from the coast, the heat was often intense and he found the blooms of spring withering more quickly than he could gather them. He grew lonely for the rush and roar of a river like the Columbia. The glare of sunlight was extremely aggravating to his eye troubles.

At the missions—Nuestra Señora de la Soledad, San Antonio de Padua, Santa Ynez Virgin y Martyr—he was greeted and accepted like royalty instead of as a mere *"hombre de educación."* A table would be laid. Then an Indian servant would lead him to the best bed in the place. In the morning, after a hearty breakfast, he would be sent on his way with a sack of provisions which often contained a whole broiled chicken, bread, cheese, hard-boiled eggs, and a flask of wine.

Douglas was fascinated by the wonderful vineyards around the missions, and by the trees of olives and figs and semi-tropical fruit. He plied the padres with questions, speaking with them in Latin, and they questioned him in turn. Although he was not a Catholic, he was impressed by the work the Fathers were doing in trying to educate and civilize the Indians, and by their own learning. Some were fine botanists and scientists. The churches, usually of adobe and redwood and tile, were the only spots of civilization in a land as primitive basically as the Oregon territory.

The natives were generally peaceful and cooperative. There was a confusion of Indian tongues, each tribe speaking a different dialect. But the tribes were generally known as Digger Indians, because they spent much of their time digging in the earth for food—nuts and roots or lizards and grubs.

Among the new pines that Douglas discovered was one which he named the *Pinus sabinii* after Joseph Sabine. Although it was a small pine, commonly known as a Digger pine, Douglas called it a "noble new species" and wrote to Sabine that he hoped it would "exist and flourish when we shall cease to be . . ."

Traveling the hot trails of the interior, feeling the sun sap his energy, Douglas often remembered the cool, moist forests of the north. When his six months in California were over, he would return there, back to the land of the Chinooks and the fur traders.

Reaching Santa Barbara in May, Douglas retraced his steps, following *El Camino Real* back to Monterey. From there, in mid-July, he traveled northward as far as the mission and settlement in San Francisco. He wanted to go farther northward in an attempt to reach the Umpqua River where he had made his search for the sugar pine, but the Russian settlement at Fort Ross, above San Francisco, was as far as he dared to go. There was no reliable trail north of there and the risk of undertaking the journey alone was too great. Reluctantly, he turned back and reached Monterey once more in August.

There he catalogued and packed his collections. At one point he noticed flakes of gold clinging to the roots of one of the California pine specimens he was preparing for shipment. Scarcely hesitating, Douglas left the gold clinging to the clotted earth around the roots. Gold was of little use to him, and it would provide extra interest for the Horticultural Society. Not that it was needed

—there were surprises enough in the seed chest and plant bundles: mariposa lilies, baby blue eyes, lilacs, gilias, poppies, lupines, and more new pines. The Monterey pine, the bristlecone fir, and the big-cone pine. Seaweeds, mosses, animal pelts and skeletons were packed along with all the rest. He divided his collection into two halves, sending one to Sabine, the other to Hooker.

He took extra satisfaction in the knowledge that no other botanist had gleaned so much and so thoroughly in California, or written descriptions of each plant found.

But it had all been gleaned at a price. His eyes bothered him more than ever. He could scarcely see to write. In a letter to Hooker, from Monterey, in November, Douglas said: "I can never read what I write, so do pardon my blunders and if you can fathom what I wish to say I am for once happy."

In Monterey, too, Douglas settled down to wait for a Hudson's Bay Company ship to take him back up the coast to Fort Vancouver. Although he kept busy with plants, time grew heavy on his hands. The winter rains kept him indoors much of the time, and the only events worth noting in his journal were his success in catching two fine trout, twenty-seven pounds each, and the failure of his search for the nest of a California condor.

The regime of Manuel Victoria had been increasingly troubled, with skirmishes and small-scale revolts among the citizens. Victoria himself had been wounded in a battle between the Californians and the Mexicans and was planning to leave the country as soon as he could travel. The former governor, Echeandía, was to replace him. But the people of Monterey appointed still a different governor.

In the confusion and scramble for power, dissatisfied factions in Monterey threatened a revolt. At the beginning of 1832, a "Company of Foreigners" was organized to help keep order, the foreigners being such men as Hartnell and Douglas, American merchants, and some of the original Spaniards. There were about fifty men in all, under Hartnell as captain.

Douglas found himself doing guard duty, a gun over his shoulder, Billy making the rounds with him.

"This is no work for a botanist," Douglas complained to his ever-sympathetic companion.

To Hartnell he declared, "The Mexican territorial government as applied to California is abominable, and that is the mildest word I can use!"

"But it's all we have," Hartnell said. "And if we don't keep a riot from starting, we won't have even that."

Spring breezes fanned Douglas' face as he patrolled, and his feet yearned for the trail again. Ship or no ship, he could not let the spring weather come and go without taking a few rambles in the fields. Although his six months' passport had long since expired, he set off for the Santa Lucia Mountains south of the village as soon as he could be spared from his guard's post.

There, and elsewhere in the area, he ransacked the hills and seashore, adding still more booty to his pack.

One day, while he was busy on the shore near the village collecting seaweed, the American consul came hurrying toward him.

"Mr. Douglas," the man called, "can you set a broken arm?"

"I'm no doctor," Douglas said, "but I can try."

The consul, Mr. Jones, explained that a boy on the Boston bark, the *Louise*, had fallen into the ship's hold, had broken his arm, and was still unconscious.

"I'll come," Douglas said.

Jones arranged for a boat, and Douglas set off with him. Billy tried to leap into the boat but Douglas sent him back. "Watch my seaweed, Billy."

On the ship, Douglas found the boy, William Davis, recovering consciousness enough to groan against the pain of his injured arm. With Jones' help, Douglas moved William to a shady portion of the deck. "Ye'll be all right, lad," he said. "It'll hurt a bit when we set the bone but, with luck, you'll have an arm as good as new."

The boy nodded, reassured by the gentleness in Douglas' voice.

Douglas' fingers were deft and in a few minutes he had a crude splint of thin pieces of wood securely wrapped by cloth on the boy's arm. "There," he said. "Don't fall again."

"I won't, doctor," William answered. "And I won't forget you, either."

The crew members, too, referred to him as "Dr. Douglas," and in the days that followed, he was amused to find that the title stuck. Wherever he went he was greeted as "Doctor." He thought: When I get back to Vancouver, I'll tell Dr. McLoughlin he has a competitor. If I ever get back.

Finally, in August, a ship arrived. It was not headed up the coast for the Columbia, but westward to the Sandwich Islands. Since the Company's ship had not come, and Douglas had lost hope that it ever would, he decided to sail with this ship and take a chance on getting another from the Islands to the Columbia.

"I've been hankering to see the Islands again, any-

how," he told the Captain. He explained that he had visited Honolulu all too briefly on his way out from England this last time.

"It's a plant-gatherer's paradise, right enough," the
captain agreed. "But you can have those volcanoes.
When they blast off, they make me shudder in my boots."

Douglas did not reply. But as he loaded his nineteen
large bundles of plants onto the ship, he resolved that
he would climb the volcanoes Mauna Loa and Mauna
Kea on the island of Hawaii if he ever had the chance.

There was still another project in his mind as he
watched the coast of California recede. Once back at the
Columbia he hoped to try returning to Europe by way
of Siberia. He had already asked permission from the
Russian authorities. In his pocket now was a letter from
Baron Wrangel, the Russian Governor of Alaska, giving
his enthusiastic approval and pledge of cooperation.

Douglas looked doubtfully at Billy, wondering if his
old terrier was up to all those miles across a frozen continent—and remembered that he, himself, had been
taken for eight years older than he was.

"We're both feeling our years, laddie," he murmured.
He looked toward the coast again. "But I've seen a lot
of the world in thirty-three years. And I'll see more."
The Sandwich Islands—the Columbia again—and then

Siberia. Siberia was a rat-trap, men said, easier to get into than out of. He felt undaunted and turned toward the blue horizon, feeling the old joy of new discovery warm his spirit.

On September 7, 1832, Douglas arrived at Honolulu. One of his first jobs was to send shipments of his plants to England on a London ship. Another ship, returning from London, brought news of an upheaval in the Horticultural Society. Joseph Sabine had resigned under a fire of criticism and a new man had been appointed in his place.

The news was tinder to Douglas' ready temper. Angrily, he sat down and scribbled off a letter, resigning as the Society's collector. From now on he would collect on his own and send everything to his old friend, Hooker. He wrote to Hooker, too, telling him of his indignation over Sabine's resignation, calling the Society "The Beastly Club" and letting his temper boil like a miniature volcano.

Plunging into activity, he set about to collect some of the magnificent island ferns for Hooker, together with a pair of Sandwich Island geese which he caught and shipped to the Zoological Society in London. But the volcanoes remained unclimbed. An attack of rheumatic

fever sent him to bed. Silently raging against the treachery of his body, he decided he would make a special
trip back to the Islands later, and explore them as he had
California. As soon as he was well enough he called on
the British Consul and made arrangements for such a
future visit.

A ship heading for the Columbia arrived. Not daring
to miss his opportunity, Douglas sailed with it, arriving
at the Columbia again in October.

There, more changes met his eye. A large schooner
was being built on the river bank. Cattle, horses, goats
and sheep ranged the rich acres. New faces greeted
Douglas, among them that of Nathaniel Wyeth, who
had come all the way from Boston to organize trade
routes throughout the Oregon territory in competition
with the Hudson's Bay Company. A school had been
built for the education of the half-breed children and
others—the first school in the Pacific Northwest.

The severe cold weather that set in with the beginning
of winter was as bitter to Douglas as ever, although now
he had his astronomical observations to keep him busy.
Everything was a subject for his inquiry—thick ice on
the river, or an eclipse of the moon.

Once the river thawed and the milder weather moved
in, Douglas was off again, to the Cowlitz River and Puget

Sound, and then to Fort Nisqually and back. He considered it all practice now for his planned trip through Siberia. He asked questions of everyone who had been to New Caledonia, the northern interior of British Columbia, which would be the scene for the first part of the long journey.

The answers were discouraging. Men spoke of the bitter cold that sometimes plunged to fifty-five degrees below zero. Food was scarce. Travelers had been known to starve, if they did not freeze first. Trading posts were few and far between and the Indians were apt to be troublesome.

"It's a white purgatory," one of the trappers told him. "There are easier ways to die."

Douglas was dismayed. It sounded like frightful country with nothing but steep mountains, a place where deer came once in a hundred years, according to the Indians.

At the fort, too, there were problems. A fever epidemic had struck, the same kind that had killed off whole villages of Indians two years earlier, together with twenty-four Company men. Around him, Indians and whites were stricken down.

Worst of all, the sight in Douglas' right eye seemed to have gone entirely. Reluctantly, he wore his goggles to protect the vision still left in his other eye. The purple glass made all plants and blooms seem the same color.

In spite of everything, he could not give up his project of traveling around the world by way of Asia. Big dreams meant big risks. He had taken such risks before and survived. Indeed, everything he had achieved had been in the face of obstacles. He would not quit now.

On March 20, he set out with the express and got as far as Fort Okanagan. From there he planned to go on with the New Caledonia horse brigade to a new territory and a new challenge.

"When we reach home," Douglas promised Billy, "I'm going to pension you off on four penny-worth of cat's meat per day. If we reach home."

Billy whined, shivering as with a blast from the cold mountains beyond.

Chapter Twelve

Red Abyss

New Caledonia was all that the fur trappers had warned. On foot or on horseback, Douglas struggled northward with the brigade—a hundred miles, five hundred, a thousand. It seemed the wilderness would go on forever. Billy whined more often, limping at Douglas' side or crouched in a boat as the brigade fought the steady current of the Fraser River. At Fort St. James, 1150 miles from Fort Vancouver, Douglas ran into a stone wall. The group that he had hoped to accompany to the Russian settlements on the seacoast, where he had been promised transportation to Siberia, could not guarantee that they would even reach the coast.

"We plan an expedition down the Skeena River," the leader of the group said, "but that's all. We may reach the sea, we may not."

Bleakly, Douglas weighed the possibilities. It was risking death to try to make the journey alone. The nearest Company post was five hundred miles away, with three hundred more miles to the Russian headquarters at Sitka. Yet, to go with the exploring party might well end in toil and trouble for nothing more than a round trip through more wilderness.

Standing at the edge of the camp, aware of the wildness of the country around him, he realized that dreams could become fantasy. A man should stretch to his utmost but his feet had to be planted on fact. To attempt to go on without the brigade would be stupidity.

"I'd rather have a devil than a dolt," the old gardener, William Beattie, had said long ago.

"We'd better not be dolts now," Douglas said to Billy. The terrier wagged his tail. "But we won't give up altogether. Back on the Columbia we'll try for a ship to Sitka. We're not licked yet."

But it was with a sense of failure that Douglas set out with a companion-assistant, William Johnson, to retrace the trail southward. They embarked in a small birchbark canoe, loaded with supplies and with Douglas' ever-present bags of seeds.

For a time all went well. Then, in a gorge on the Fraser River, the waters struck out viciously, whirling the light craft in the rapids, driving it toward small islands of rock.

Douglas, in the prow, felt the impact first as the canoe struck. He heard Johnson shout, and turned to see water pouring into the craft—over the seed boxes, his diary, his box of instruments, his notes.

"Try for the shore!" he yelled. "If we—" Before he could say more, the whirling water sucked him under. Flailing his arms, he came up to the surface again to see Johnson crawling onto one of the rocks, Billy beside him. Then there was only foam and rushing water and rocks again as the rapids swept him onward. The smashed canoe washed past him, its contents spilling out into the water. A black object spun past—his diary for Hooker. He reached for it but his fingers closed only on foam.

From then on there was no time for anything except a battle for life. Struggling to keep his head above the surface, gasping for air, Douglas felt the river carrying him into the whirlpool below the rapids.

Vainly he fought against the eddies, trying to reach a rock where he could haul himself out. Several times he managed to get inches from the rocky shore before the water seized him and carried him back into its dizzy center.

He lost all sense of time. The world was reduced to a turbulent pool in which he was swept around and around like a doll. When he was finally swept onto the shore, he hardly realized it and lay, still making swimming motions, against the stones.

White-faced, Johnson reached him at last and knelt down. "Mister Douglas, are you hurt?"

He sat up, moaning, rubbing his bruised body. "We lost everything, didn't we?"

"Everything but our lives. I wouldn't have given a penny for yours during that hour and a half you were in the water."

"An hour and a half!" Douglas let the information sink in while he warded off Billy's over-eager demonstrations of affection. "Well, Johnson, we'll be spending many more hours on foot, until we can get another canoe." He got up and limped toward higher ground to start a fire. The canoe could be replaced but not the four hundred plants, nor the journals and instruments, the food and the blankets.

Shivering, Douglas thought of the arduous miles ahead. He and Johnson would have to live like savages. Perhaps they would be happy enough to eat grubs and lizards before they were through.

"Miserable country!" Johnson snarled.

Douglas looked at the river where he had so nearly drowned. "No, Johnson. Beautiful country. On the whole I have been fortunate and my accidents few."

Johnson looked at him in wonder. The dripping, half-drowned Scotsman had just lost everything he prized and yet he could call this a beautiful country. Johnson shook his head, not understanding.

They got back to Fort Vancouver in August. Seared with sun and wind, broken in body and spirit, Douglas led the way from the landing place up to McLoughlin's establishment. Exposure and near-starvation had taken such a toll, plus his sorrow at losing most of the summer to a struggle for bare survival, that his dreams for the moment were almost at the vanishing point.

As he recuperated at the fort, he thought over his trip to Siberia once again, then finally gave up. There was too much against him, including his own worn-out condition. Gradually, new plans took the place of the abandoned ones. He would botanize some more here, and then return to Hawaii.

"You can sleep under the palms there, Billy," he told his dog, "while I stuff my seed bag, and climb Mauna Loa."

The shining summit of Mount Hood to the south,

Mount St. Helens to the north, beckoned to him, and he added: "First I'll try these slopes. Their snow should cool my feet against the heat of those craters in the Islands."

He had not come to the Oregon territory to be a mountaineer but he had become one, even as he had become a geographer and zoologist. Though he did not reach the peak of Mount Hood, he was the first to attempt it, as he had been first to climb any of the Canadian Rocky Mountains, the Cascades, or the Blue Mountains of Oregon.

In his journal, he wrote: "To console myself for the want of friends of a kindred feeling in this distant land, for an exchange of sympathy or advice, I vary my amusements; by day it is a barren place that does not afford me a blade of grass, a bird, or a rock, before unnoticed, from which I derive inexpressible delight, while during the stillness of a cloudless night their localities are determined, altitudes measured, the climate they breathe analyzed. Thank God my heart feels gladness in these operations."

He had such gladness often in the land he was leaving. The joy of discovery made up for the troubles and pain. In the Islands, who knew what other exciting discoveries awaited him?

Douglas left the Columbia in October, 1833, sailing toward the Islands by way of San Francisco.

"My whole life is ahead of me yet," he thought aloud. He was only thirty-four. Full of plans, he turned his back on the misty outlines of Northwest America for the last time.

The land that came in view in late December as the *Dryad* neared the Islands was far different from that which Douglas had left. Looking westward, he saw the dim shape of Oahu, twenty miles distant, where the harbor of Honolulu provided anchorage for vessels from Boston, China, and Europe. Seen from twenty miles away the island looked grim and barren, its sun-scorched peaks lifeless. Douglas recalled his first disappointment at the sight—and the following thrill as foliage and green chasms began to appear. Slowly the barren peaks softened and the true brilliance and richness of the island appeared: forests, waterfalls, the rugged sides of the promontory Diamond Head softened at their base in a maze of green vegetation and lines of coconut palms.

Once the ship was through the channel in the coral reef girdling the harbor, natives in outrigger canoes appeared. Nearer shore, where combers rolled in with a soft roar, brown men, women, and children rode surf boards. On shore itself, the town was a conglomeration of grass huts, ugly wooden stores, hotels, and saloons built by enterprising white men. There were also several grass-thatched chapels that American missionaries were beginning to build in an attempt to Christianize the Islanders.

Douglas' glance roved from the city to the wilderness of green above and beyond, then southward, in the direction of the largest of the islands in the chain, Hawaii. It was there that Mauna Kea, the highest island mountain in the world, lifted its white summit into the intensely blue sky. There, Mauna Loa, too, rose to almost the same height. Douglas wanted to lose no time in scaling the volcanic giants, but first there was Christmas to be celebrated and plans made. The British consul at Honolulu, Richard Charlton, had promised to be of help when Douglas had called on him two years earlier.

As he put ashore with Billy and his fellow passengers, the few forlorn Christmas decorations here and there in the Yankee shops made Douglas think of Christmas in Scotland. Next year, he promised himself, he would spend Christmas at home by his own hearth. Perhaps by then he would be ready to settle down to the life of a gardener or curator, for, in spite of his anticipation at the thought of forthcoming adventures, he felt a deep, physical weariness. It was time for Billy to settle down, too.

Consul Charlton greeted Douglas warmly and offered him the hospitality of his own house. There Douglas spent Christmas Day and made his plans for continuing his journey. Two days later he took an American schooner for Hawaii.

It was the second day of the New Year, 1834, when the schooner put into the blue, surf-braceleted bay of Hilo, Hawaii. Again the familiar grass huts appeared, looking like green haystacks, and the same wavy lines of coconut palms, together with tree ferns and bougainvillea in purple or red masses over verandahs, bright hibiscus, begonias, and natives wearing leis of jasmine and gardenia around their necks. Crowning all were the peaks of Mauna Kea and Mauna Loa. Four thousand feet up on the flank of Mauna Loa was Kilauea, the largest active volcano in the world.

At the home of a pioneer American missionary, the Rev. Joseph Goodrich, Douglas talked of scarcely anything but his plan to climb to all three summits. Goodrich had climbed Mauna Kea—the White Mountain— and advised Douglas as to the route. He also helped get a guide and carriers for the twenty-five-mile ascent. Five were to carry Douglas' supplies, and eleven others

to carry their own equipment, including great quantities
of *poi*, the staple food of the Islanders.

"These people," Rev. Goodrich said, "can store away
more food than a bee can honey."

"I can tell that by their waistlines," Douglas commented. Fatness was a sign of beauty among the natives,
and great bowls or calabashes of the paste-like *poi*, eaten
with the fingers, helped put pounds of flesh on both
men and women. Extremely fat women, some dressed in
sack-like dresses and others in native bark skirts, rode
astride lean and underfed horses which they handled
with the skill of the Nez Percé Indians. Horses, the Rev.
Goodrich told Douglas, had not been brought to the
Islands until 1803; when they were, the Hawaiians had
become horse mad.

There were no horses or mules on the climb up Mauna
Kea. In single file, led by the native guide and interpreter, Honolii, Douglas' party started its ascent on
January 7. Douglas carried sixty pounds on his own
back. Only Billy went unburdened.

The first part of the climb was through a plantation
belt where breadfruit and sugar cane, mango and taro
trees, grew thickly. Next came the deep woods where
great acacia trees intercepted the damp sunlight and

made flickering shadows on the undergrowth. Violets
several feet high lifted their blooms among wild ginger
plants. Giant ferns with stems thick as a man's arm grew
forty feet high, their fronds dripping from the most
recent rain. For the rains came often and the path Douglas followed was so soft that he sank many times over
his knees. Candlenut trees, guava, and myrtle added
their lushness to the terrain. In places, great networks
of vines and interlaced ferns blocked the path entirely.
In others, rushing creeks cut across the trail.

As if there had not been enough rain before, fresh
rain came to drip from Douglas' hat and his clothing
and his heavy knapsack. In the middle of the downpour,
something bolted across the path so close to him that he
jerked back. Just ahead, Honolii stopped with the same
suddenness, bringing his gun into position. Before Honolii could fire, a lean, fierce-eyed animal tossed its crum-
pled horns, snorted, and crashed into the undergrowth.

Honolii shrugged and put his gun back on his shoulder. "Many wild cattle in mountains. Wild black pigs,
also. Men trap cow, bulls, in pits. Sell the hides and
tallow. Good business."

They went on through the rain, climbing steadily but
slowly, giving Douglas a chance to study the foliage.
The best thing about the rain, he thought, was that it

gave his eyes a rest from the brilliant glare of the sun. But it was no help to the rheumatism that had begun in far away New York and still bothered him when he was wet or chilled.

That night they ate dinner at a sawmill on the mountainside, then slept in some adjacent huts, but there was no dry fuel. In the morning they were as damp as before, and the rain was still falling. The ragged dome above was invisible through the clouds hanging around its waist. Near the end of the cloud belt, Douglas jerked to a stop again. A few rods away was a large, odd plant, its head made of stiff, dagger-like leaves. He forgot the rain and cold and his tired muscles. What a gift a parcel of the seeds of the silver-sword plant would be for Hooker, along with all the species of ferns he would add! His pleasure at finding the sword plant and a strange, prickly pine, warmed his blood for an hour or so. By nightfall, however, he was shivering like his companions and glad to crawl into a cattle hunter's lodge for shelter.

Before the final climb to the summit, two days were spent along the grassy slopes for more botanizing and for a look at some of the extinct volcanic peaks. Honolii had better luck with his rifle here and shot one of the wild bulls to add to their food supply.

The forest ceased at about six thousand feet, followed

by stingy vegetation of scrub and brush and ending with gray wormwood and coarse tufts of grass. The air grew drier as the fogs and rainclouds fell away beneath them. The sun beating on bare rocks where only patches of orange lichen grew sent its painful darts into Douglas' eyes once more.

It was January 11, four days after the departure from Hilo, that Douglas set off early in the morning for the summit, leaving Billy at the camp. With him were three of the Islanders and two Americans from the sawmill where the group had first stopped. Douglas was astonished to find ferns growing in the fissures of old lava. Portions of the mountain were covered with ancient congealed and jagged lava so sharp that it was impossible to travel across it. In other places, gray stretches of smoother lava, *pahoehoe* or satin rock, extended in wrinkles and folds, coils and serpentine streams.

The cold grew intense at heights of eleven and twelve thousand feet, and now there were no plants, no birds, no wild life of any kind to tempt Douglas from his goal of the summit. A weird landscape of tuna cones, basalt, clinkers, and fine ash took over where the lava beds left off. Valleys gashed into the slope were filled with snow and the sun glancing off the snow glinted with a thousand sharp-tipped arrows against Douglas' eyes, making them bloodshot, his eyelids stiff. The dryness of the air made his skin feel withered, and in the thin atmosphere his pulse beat rapidly.

At ten o'clock the summit was reached. Breathless, Douglas stood in the deep snow that covered the cones and the volcanic ash of the highest peak of the Pacific, 13,784 feet above the sea.

Aside from his own quick breathing, and that of the others, there was not a sound, not even the tiny whir of an insect. Above, the sun shone. Below, clouds hung in mighty clots and vapors, like another ocean. Douglas felt a terrible humility and reverence. This was a geologist's world, not a botanist's, but it was inspiring in its very desolation.

He was eager to use his new skill in barometric observation, and he got busy with his instruments. Even where no animals, birds, or plants existed, there were still a hundred curiosities and marvels. The day wore on, and when he finally made his way back down to the camp again at dusk, he felt that the laborious ascent had been more than worthwhile. Even when his skin began to peel from his face and hands, from the sun-shot dryness of the air, he bore it philosophically.

On his way back down to Hilo, he stuffed his sack

full of fern specimens, mosses, and seeds, tying the plants in bundles protected by bark so that they would not ferment. One fern was so much like a species that grew in Scotland that for an instant he could imagine he was back on some Highland slope.

Again in Hilo, he took only enough time to pack and preserve the plants he had collected before he was off once more, this time to the active volcano of Kilauea. Again the interpreter Honolii went with him, nine other natives helping with the food and supplies. Each native cut off a stalk of sugar cane to use as a staff. During rest stops on the journey, they peeled and bit off an inch or two of the staff with their strong teeth to quench their thirst.

The first morning out, after a stay at a native hut, Douglas was glad that he had left Billy behind. For as he got up and dressed, he saw an old woman nearby feeding her dog. She had a calabash of *poi* in front of her and this she was busily cramming into the dog's mouth. At first Douglas mistook this for kindness but Honolii enlightened him.

"Old woman fatten dog for feast," the guide said.

A few minutes later, the native who had been their host, went to the door of the hut and gave a series of strange, grunting calls. There was an answering grunt

from some nearby fern trees and suddenly a large, black
pig ran out. The native killed the pig and carried it to a
pit of heated stones.

"We carry roast pig up to the Lake of Everlasting
Fire," Honolii said. He rubbed his belly. "In here."

Honolii, who had been educated by white men and
had learned their language, seemed to be poking fun at
the superstition that had once surrounded the crater in
Kilauea's flank. There, according to legend, the dread
goddess Pelé had ruled, governing the eruptions of the
volcano so that natives did not dare approach without
making offerings. At one time, great numbers of pigs
were thrown into the lava to appease her.

That afternoon, as Douglas stood on the west side of
the giant and fiery abyss of Kilauea he could understand
why the natives had felt such fear. Although the crater
was comparatively tranquil now, it still had power to
make goose pimples rise on his arms as he sat at its
edge and gazed at the pit that was nine miles in circumference. Around its margin, cracks and cones let
out steam and jets of sulphurous vapor. In the pit, a lake
of liquid fire extended over a portion of the crater, a
bubbling and hissing mass with boiling fountains of lava
that spouted forty to seventy feet into the air. The lurid
surface was in constant motion. Another smaller lake in

the great crater boiled like soup. All around, the air was filled with hissings and cracklings, a din so great that Douglas knew he could never describe it.

That night, pitching his tent about twenty yards back from the crater's edge, he watched the sun set, its own golden fires seeming pale in contrast to the fires of the crater. And when the moon rose it seemed a pale blue. It was a perfect night for astronomical observations but for once the lure of beauty was stronger than that of science. Douglas could not take his eyes from the scene long enough to sight the stars with his instruments.

The next afternoon, with three men, he descended several hundred feet into the crater and to the edge of a black shelf. Below the shelf the twisted lava formed gray lakes and rivers, ridges and peaks, frozen whirlpools and chasms streaked yellow with sulphur or white with alum. Everywhere there were fissures steaming and crackling. In one of the crevices Douglas picked up a strange bit of lava that was like yellow spun glass, called "Pelé's hair." The heat burned the soles of his feet through his shoes, and the lava felt hollow so that he shuddered with visions of plunging into a wrinkled vat of flames below. Beside him, Honolii coughed from the fumes; Douglas felt a violent headache spreading through his own skull.

Still he stayed, spending two hours, estimating the lava flow, jotting notes on the height of the volcano, circling the whole circumference, torn between sensations of horror and religious wonder.

Taking a final look at the furnace of desolation and magnificence, he marveled at his own presence here—so far from the cool and gentle mists of his homeland, so far from green and growing life.

Holding his hand to his throbbing head, he thought: One day here is worth a year of common existence.

Another challenge awaited Douglas. He had not yet climbed Mauna Loa, the Long Mountain.

Five days after his descent of Kilauea, he again stood on a summit, this time that of Mauna Loa, the world's largest single land mass, tilting most of northern Hawaii upward to the great dome of ghostly, volcanic tableland covered with ash and lava and snow. Billy was with Douglas this time. With their guide, Calipio, they had raced to the top, leaving two fearful Islanders behind.

"*Kauka* is too fast," the other natives said later, calling him by the name which meant "doctor."

Too fast? Douglas wondered briefly. Perhaps. He had still not learned patience but drove at everything as if pushed by a mighty hand. Still, to stand where only one

other white man had ever stood before—Archibald
Menzies who had climbed this slope forty years before—
was the reward.

Descending, Douglas faced the unrewarding aspects
of his climb. His legs trembled. His eyes ached bitterly.
At moments his vision and even his brain swam.

Well, now he would rest and restore his strength,
while he wrote his notes on the volcanoes and continued
his botanizing in greener regions. If there were time,
he would classify the plants of Hawaii according to their
life zones.

In spite of his resolution, he was back at Kilauea a
few days later, measuring the depth of the pit and collecting lava specimens.

At the end of March he returned to Honolulu to wait
for a ship to England. He waited until late June and still
no ship came.

Two longings pulled at him: the desire to breathe
the air of his native land again and a nagging desire to
look once more at the crater of Kilauea. "I must return
to the volcano," he thought often, repeating the words
he had written from Hilo to Mrs. Charlton, "if it is only
to look—to look and admire."

In Honolulu, he met a chaplain, the Rev. John Diell,
who had come recently from the United States. Diell,

excited by Douglas' accounts of the Hawaiian volcanoes, suggested that they go together to climb Kilauea.

"I'll take my wife and child along," Diell said. "They can stay in Hilo while we scout the crater. And my servant John will be a help. There's a schooner leaving on the third of July."

The two men were standing near the waterfront with a clear view of the harbor. An English vessel was not expected for several weeks. Still, there was no way to be sure. One thing was evident, however. No English ship rode at anchor now, nor was there a mast or sail on the sparkling blue of the sea.

"I'll go with you," Douglas said. "You take your family, I'll take my dog."

The decision made, he felt his spirits quicken. One more adventure and then when it was over, perhaps the ship would be waiting to carry him home.

Green Testament

As the schooner bearing the Diell family and Douglas made its way among the islands toward Hawaii, Mr. Diell announced a change of plans.

"If it won't inconvenience you greatly," he said to Douglas, "I'd like to pay a visit to the island of Molokai. So I'm thinking of leaving the ship at Lahaina. You're welcome to join me and the family, if you like."

"Thank you, but I'm eager to get to Hawaii," Douglas answered. "I'll go on."

"Then I'll meet you there in a few days, at Hilo."

Douglas agreed, thinking no more about it. The Diells left the ship at Lahaina. Then, as the schooner put to sea again, Douglas was startled to see Diell's dark-skinned servant still on board.

"What's wrong, John?" he asked the man. "I thought you were going with your master."

Nervously John explained that he had become confused ashore and had got back on the wrong ship. "And here I am," he added miserably. He looked toward shore, as if he planned to jump overboard and swim.

"Don't worry about it," Douglas said. "You can go along with me, and we'll explain it to Mr. Diell when we meet him later."

John stammered his gratitude. He attached himself to Douglas, following at his heels almost as faithfully as Billy.

The schooner was detained at Kohala Point at the northern end of Hawaii. Douglas, fretting with fresh impatience, and seeing a way to add extra adventure, decided to land and hike over Mauna Kea to Hilo.

"Then I'll go with you," announced John when Douglas told him his plan. "I can help carry stuff, like them science instruments."

"That would be a help. Billy's not much good when it comes to carrying."

So the two put ashore and set off over a trail that followed the northern and eastern slopes of the mountain for close to a hundred miles.

Douglas set a leisurely pace for it was obvious that for all his willingness, John was not a born climber, and the road led steadily upward. They followed a meandering path, pausing to study whatever interested Douglas. John was a good companion, interested in Douglas' bits of information about the plants.

The first night they camped under the stars, sharing Douglas' blanket between them, with Billy fighting for a corner. Douglas felt there was something healing and restoring about starlight. The stars' radiance never stung his eyes as the sun's did. Even his rheumatism bothered him less than it had for months, in spite of the rains. Feeling the hard flank of Mauna Loa under him, he remembered again the nights in the Highlands with Hooker and Scouler, the days in the gardens back at Scone, and the more recent days and nights at the Columbia. There the muffled roar of the river had lulled him to sleep. He thought of the flickering campfires, the high music of the pines, and always the beckoning plants, perfumed blossoms, seed pods fat as a rich man's purse.

He breathed deeply with contentment. The richest man in the world had never carried the perpetual, self-renewing treasures that were almost daily on his back. In each tiny seed was the promise of a root, a stem, leaves, buds, and finally a flower—a mighty flower like the sugar pine he had discovered, or as tiny as the baby blue-eyes he had found in California. Hooker's latest letters had been full of astonishment at the harvest of seeds that kept coming by almost every ship to England.

"What a glorious collection!" Hooker had written of the California shipment. "I think I scarcely ever in a collection of such an extent saw so much that is new and rare."

If only a man could collect the light of the stars or the sound of the river, Douglas thought, to take them back to Perth.

When he fell asleep, he dreamed that he was wading through fields of the flowers and shrubs and trees he had discovered. They grew for miles over the slope of the earth . . . lilies, huckleberries, clovers, currants, pines, cherries, firs, apples, honeysuckles, peonies, orchids, flax. . . .

He awoke to morning and the fringed head of Billy poking at him, the moist tongue lapping at his cheek.

Douglas looked at the dog and laughed. "You are something of a gray peony yourself, lad. Be careful, or I'll tuck you in my vasculum."

That day, Douglas unconsciously moved faster. He could not remember when he had felt better. His dream still clung to him pleasantly, making even the rocky and more difficult part of the trail seem easier. It was not until midday that he realized that John was not in sight behind him. He stopped and turned back.

He found his companion sitting beside the trail, his shoes off, a look of misery on his face.

"I'm half in my grave," John groaned.

"I'm sorry. I did not realize I was striding along so fast."

"It ain't that, sir. It's my feet."

Douglas looked. Broken blisters covered John's heels, the skin raw underneath. "You can't keep going on feet like those, man." He straightened, trying to think what should be done.

"You ain't gonna leave me here, sir?"

Douglas shook his head. "Just before I turned back, I thought I saw a native hut about a quarter of a league off. If you can make it there, you can rest up and either I or Mr. Diell will send a guide back for you."

"Who'll carry for you?" John asked worriedly.

Douglas smiled, putting a hand under John's elbow and helping him up. "I'll tell you. I've got a pack horse but you can't see him. His name's David Douglas." He took the load from John's shoulder and added it to the bundle he was already carrying. "Come along now. We'll take it slowly."

When they reached the grass shack and found a native family there, Douglas managed to make them understand he wanted John to rest there for a few days. He offered some cloth, a comb, and a pair of scissors in payment.

Unexpectedly, tears came to John's dark eyes when the moment came for Douglas to leave. He seized Douglas' hand. "I don't like it to see you go off alone, sir, without nobody to watch out for you or tote your things."

Douglas was touched but he said gruffly, "Nonsense, lad. In a tame land like this there's nothing to worry about. You worry about those blisters."

He left, going swiftly, his heavy load arching his shoulders. "We're really alone now, aren't we, Billy?" he said. "It isn't the first time."

That night, Douglas found shelter and a dry roof at a ranch. In the morning he stopped at a hut owned by an English cattle hunter, Edward Gurney. The hut stood at a spot where the trail Douglas was following crossed another. Uncertain as to his direction, Douglas asked Gurney the best way to proceed.

"To Hilo?" Gurney said. "Some of the natives who work for me here are going that way soon, maybe tomorrow, and you can go with them. If you want to wait over, they'll show you."

"Tomorrow?"

"Or the next day."

Douglas considered. He had already lost more time than he intended and he should be at Hilo when Mr. Diell arrived. "If you could point out the way, yourself, I think I'd better move on."

"I'll walk a ways with you," Gurney said and started off down the trail.

As they walked, Douglas told the man a little about himself and his reason for being there. "This will be my last trip for awhile," he concluded. "I'm sailing home to Scotland. Billy and I are going to settle down."

At the end of a mile, Gurney stopped. "Follow this trail from here, then when you reach the Kapoholimuele Gulch, take the fork to the left."

"Thanks," Douglas said, shifting his load higher on his shoulders. "Are there any natives along the way? I'd like to hire someone to help me carry my things."

"There may be some by the bull pits. You want to steer clear of those, by the way. There are a couple of pits right on your route. The first one's about two and a half miles ahead, near a pond. You won't see it if you don't look close. So keep an eye out."

"I will," Douglas said. He thanked the man again and went on. As the cattle rancher said, a person could easily stumble into one of those pits made for trapping the wild bulls. The pits were camouflaged with grass and branches to look like the surrounding earth. A wild bull stepping upon the false support would crash to the bottom of the deep hole and be trapped.

Nearing the spot which Gurney had indicated, Douglas walked with caution, inspecting the trail ahead carefully. Billy sensed his caution and lagged at his heels.

"There it is!" Douglas said. His botanist's eye had quickly detected the slightly paler hue of the grass strewn around the pit, and the drooping aspect of leaves mixed in, in spite of the cunning with which fresh vines had been drawn over everything.

"Nay—stay back, Billy." It might support the terrier's weight and it might not. "I don't want to have to crawl down and try to get you out if you spill over the side."

Together they circled the pit, then followed the trail again.

Reaching the second pit, which had a hole torn in the covering, Douglas saw three natives standing at its edge, and heard the snorting rage of a wild bull.

He paused at the edge, watching the antics of the infuriated creature as it pawed the earth and tore at the walls of its prison with its heavy horns. The bloodshot eyes uprolled toward his, fiery with rage and desperation.

A volcano in each eye, Douglas thought. He turned
to the natives, indicating by gestures that he wished to
hire one of them to help him carry his burden to Hilo.

The natives shook their heads and pointed at the bull,
indicating that they had business to attend to.

Resigned, Douglas trudged on. If he kept up a good
pace, he might reach Hilo by evening. It was still early
and the weather was fine for hiking, a faint mist having
cooled the sunlight. It was the kind of a day that had
so often lured him from his school desk and on to Kinnoul, long ago.

He had not gone far when he heard the snorting of
another wild bull. Pausing, he saw ahead of him a third
bullock pit, the grass and branches gaping where the
bull had plunged through. There were no natives at
this pit.

Putting his bundle down, Douglas approached the
pit's edge to have a look at the animal. The mist was
thinner here, the sunlight striking down against the
edges of the pit so that the darkness was rimmed with a
circle of gold.

Billy stood back, his hair bristling, while Douglas
peered over the pit's edge.

This bull was even larger than the other, Douglas
observed, and it was all one storming, snorting volcano,
its nostrils distended. The rank odor of the bull came

up to him, together with the sweet but heavy odor of the dying grass.

Douglas turned away, then paused, a violent pain darting through his eyes. Who would think the brilliance was so strong? Looking upward, he had a hazy notion that one ray of sunlight, more powerful than all others, was aiming at him from the most glittering snowfield on the summit of Mauna Loa. He put his hand to his eyes, dazzled—and heard a crackling underfoot.

His vision cleared and he had one breathless glimpse of Billy standing off, waiting, and of one white flower growing at the pit's edge, fresh among the wilted grasses.

The world fell apart under his feet, tearing like cloth. Wind seemed to rush up around his knees. He reached out to stop his plunge, clutching at the raw earth for a handhold. One hand closed on a sheaf of loose grass, dragging it with him down into the huge and bellowing darkness.

The dog ran to the pit's edge, then howled and ran a few feet away. Again he returned, quivering, staring first at the pit and then at the sky. He lifted his muzzle and howled for minutes at a time. Finally, he trotted toward the big bundle lying beyond the pit and sniffed at it: familiar smell of oilcloth and botanical papers, metal smell of instruments and vasculum, man-smell of an old shirt, the thin fragrance of tea, dew-smell of a damp blanket. . . .

Once more the terrier went back to the pit and howled before he returned to the knapsack and lay down beside it, his chin against the earth, his gaze fixed on the bundle, waiting.

The Hawaiian sun rose higher, lighting the dome of the mountain. On the mountain's flank, the crater of Kilauea burned as before. In the pit, silent now except for the low grunt of the bull, Douglas' broken watch ticked on.

At ten, three natives came to the pit. One saw a bit of torn clothing clinging to one of the branches over the pit. The natives came nearer and looked down for a long while. They turned finally, and ran back up the trail to Gurney's ranch. One of them, however, stopped and pointed at Billy crouched by the knapsack. He approached the dog, reaching toward the bundle.

Billy stayed as he was but a growl trembled in his throat. The native took another look at the dog's warning eyes and rejoined his companions.

"The dog cry," the Islander said. "He not let anyone touch bundle. Bundle of gold, maybe."

Billy waited. Even when the natives came back with Gurney, shot the bull, and lifted Douglas' body from the pit, the dog continued to guard his bundle. Finally, after much coaxing, Gurney managed to lure him away. A native picked up the bundle and started down the trail, while three others gently shouldered the remains of *Kauka* wrapped in a bullock hide, and began the twenty-seven mile march to the sea.

Gurney followed, calling softly to Billy. The terrier came after many pauses and backward glances.

Gurney patted him roughly. "It looks like, when the time comes, you'll be sailin' to Scotland alone. I reckon the consul will see to it."

When Gurney went on, Billy trotted heavily behind him.

HERE LIES

Master DAVID DOUGLAS

BORN IN SCOTLAND
A.D. 1799

AN INDEFATIGABLE TRAVELLER,
HE WAS SENT OUT BY
THE ROYAL HORTICULTURAL SOCIETY OF LONDON,
AND GAVE HIS LIFE FOR SCIENCE
IN THE WILDS OF HAWAII,

July 12, 1834

E'en here the tear of pity springs
And hearts are touched by human things.
VIRGIL

These words are engraved on a bronze plaque in the vestibule of the Kawaiahao church at Honolulu; a translation from the Latin which was originally engraved on a tombstone set up outside the church wall. In the Scone churchyard in Perth, a twenty-three-foot monument preserves the memory of David Douglas, relating his accomplishments and praising his memory. On the back of the stone are listed some of the trees and shrubs and plants introduced by him. To list them all would have taken a monument much larger. Of the countless species he collected, 215 were new discoveries, including the sugar pine, *Pinus lambertiana*, the biggest pine tree in the world. Another great tree, the tallest in America, next to the sequoia, is the tree that bears Douglas' name, the Douglas fir. It was first reported by Archibald Menzies and was called *Pinus taxifolia*, but it was thanks to Douglas that its seeds were collected and brought to Europe. Joseph Sabine named it *Pinus douglasii*; it is now known as *Pseudotsuga taxifolia*. In the pages of plant catalogues or dictionaries many another bloom or shrub or herb has the Latinized version of his name written after it: *douglasii*.

Botanist, mountaineer, zoologist, he pioneered the way for later scientists and pried open the treasure box of the wilderness so that a whole world could see and cultivate its rich fruits.

More enduring than all the written tributes Douglas received after his death, or those engraved in marble, are the acres of beauty he left to the world. There is scarcely a garden anywhere that does not contain at least one of the flowers he introduced. They were started from the seeds he carried on his back along the Columbia, the Umpqua, the Willamette, over the Rockies, the Blue Mountains, the Coast Ranges, and the volcanoes of Hawaii.

The flowers, and the pines and firs whose cones jostled in his knapsack, are his green and enduring testament.

"Thank God that my heart feels gladness in these operations," Douglas said, and shared the gladness with the world.